Illustrated by François Thisdale

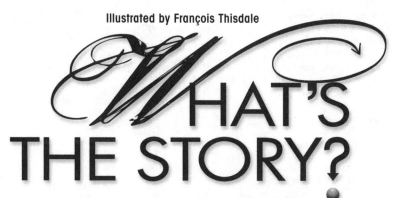

WHAT'S THE STORY?

Margaret-Anne Colgan
Voula Plagakis
Leena M. Sandblom

D1038681

LES ÉDITIONS
CEC
Une compagnie de Quebecor Media

9001, boul. Louis-H.-La Fontaine, Anjou (Québec) Canada H1J 2C5
Téléphone : 514-351-6010 • Télécopieur : 514-351-3534

Editorial Management
Carolyn Faust

Production Management
Danielle Latendresse

Production Coordination
Rodolphe Courcy

Editorial Coordination
Nancy Schmidt

Graphic Coordination
Louise Chabot

Rights Research
Monique Rosevear

Cover and Page Design

Illustrator
François Thisdale

Les Éditions CEC inc. remercient le gouvernement du Québec de l'aide financière accordée à l'édition de cet ouvrage par l'entremise du Programme de crédit d'impôt pour l'édition de livres, administré par la SODEC.

Turning Point, What's the Story?
© 2009, Les Éditions CEC inc.
9001, boul. Louis-H.-La Fontaine
Anjou (Québec) H1J 2C5

Dépôt légal : 2009
Bibliothèque et Archives nationales du Québec
Bibliothèque et Archives Canada

ISBN : 978-2-7617-2868-3

Imprimé au Canada
1 2 3 4 5 12 11 10 09

PHOTO SOURCES

Alamy:
P. 38: AAFKCG (Jodi Picoult)

Getty:
P. 57: 200561503-001 (Haiti),
P. 71: 3334453 (Mentone),
P. 98: HN3576-001 (train crash)

iStockphoto:
3459065*

shutterstock:
16343464*, 8395273*, 21357958*,
12918334*, 23605822*, P. 91: 452211
(married couple)

Topfoto:
P. 2: 1070913 (Roald Dahl),
P. 88: gr0049373_H (Kate Chopin)

Other sources:
P. 22: (M. E. Kerr), courtesy of Zoe
Kamitses. P. 54: (Edwidge Danticat),
http://en.wikipedia.org/wiki/File:Edwidge_
Danticat_by_David_Shankbone.jpg GNU
FDL. P. 68: (Mark Twain), public domain.

*background images

TEXT SOURCES

PP. 6–17: "Lamb to the Slaughter"
by Roald Dahl, from Someone Like You,
Publishers: David Higham and Michael
Joseph.

PP. 26–34: "I've Got Gloria" © 1997 by
M. E. Kerr, from No Easy Answers: Short
Stories About Making Tough Choices by
Donald Gallo, editor. Used by permission
of Random House Children's Books, a
division of Random House, Inc.

PP. 42–49: Reprinted with the permission of
ATRIA BOOKS, a Division of Simon and
Schuster, Inc., from My Sister's Keeper
by Jodi Picoult. © 2004 by Jodi Picoult.
All rights reserved.

PP. 58–63: From The Dew Breaker by
Edwidge Danticat, © 2004 by Edwidge
Danticat. Used by permission of Alfred A.
Knopf, a division of Random House, Inc.

PP. 72–82: "Is He Living or Is He Dead?"
by Mark Twain, public domain.

PP. 92–95: "The Story of an Hour"
by Kate Chopin, public domain.

Table of Contents

ABOUT THE ILLUSTRATOR ··IV

CHAPTER 1 LAMB TO THE SLAUGHTER by Roald Dahl ································1

CHAPTER 2 I'VE GOT GLORIA by M. E. Kerr ································21

CHAPTER 3 MY SISTER'S KEEPER by Jodi Picoult································37

CHAPTER 4 THE DEW BREAKER by Edwidge Danticat ································53

CHAPTER 5 IS HE LIVING OR IS HE DEAD? by Mark Twain ································67

SUPPLEMENTARY STORY

THE STORY OF AN HOUR by Kate Chopin ································87

François Thisdale

François Thisdale is an award-winning freelance illustrator. His eye-catching style combines traditional drawing and painting with computer imagery. When François is not creating art, he's writing stories and composing music.

Born: January 8, 1964, Montréal, Québec

Quote: "My work is my passion. It demands a lot from me, but I love it. And my reward? I'm achieving my dreams."

More about François Thisdale

- As a child, François was always creating art. In elementary school, he entertained his friends with sketches of hockey players and comic book heroes.
- His father was a musician and his mother was an amateur painter.
- During his teenage years, both of his parents encouraged him to follow his dream of becoming an artist.
- At the age of 17, François went to CEGEP to study graphic art. Although he never worked as a graphic designer, the skills he learned there helped him to develop his artistic style.
- Over his 22-year career, François has drawn thousands of illustrations and worked for clients in Canada, the USA, France, Argentina and Korea.
- Today, he lives close to Montréal in the town of Carignan, with his wife and daughter, Nini, who he calls "a marvelous girl."

Favourite illustration:
Of all the illustrations François has created, his favourite is the one he produced for the book *La nuit des mystères*. Here's why:

"I love this illustration because I enjoyed working on this book, and it reminds me of that experience. The story was superb and I was free to create what I wanted. I enjoy the mood that exists between these two wolves and the love that is reflected here. And there's one more reason why this illustration is my favourite: the eyes of the wolf at the top left are inspired by the eyes of my daughter."

Awards include:
- 2004 Vision Awards Annual Report Competition Platinum Award from the League of American Communications Professionals
- 2005 TD Canadian Children's Literature Award finalist
  This is the largest children's publishing and literature prize in Canada.

Works include:
Illustrations for:
- children's books
- book covers
- magazines
- corporate reports
- school textbooks

A children's book:
- story and illustrations

Soundtracks for:
- films
- TV
- exhibits

Questions and answers:

Q: François, which story in this anthology did you like the most?

Lamb to the Slaughter

Q: Why?

I love mysteries and Roald Dahl's sense of irony.

Q: How did you get your ideas for these beautiful illustrations?

I read the stories and absorbed their message, style, and mood. Then I imagined images that could express the key points in the plots.

Q: Did you change your artistic style to create the illustrations for this book?

No. The essence of my artistic style does not change, but I did adapt it to meet the needs of this project.

Q: How did you create the illustrations?

I took several steps ...

- *First, I drew pencil sketches of the images.*
- *Then, I painted the sketches, using acrylics and watercolours, and I used photos too.*
- *Finally, I altered the combined art/photo works with computer software. I used everything I could in the creative process to help me reach a balance between the feeling of a painting and the feeling of a photograph.*

Q: What was your ultimate goal?

To set the mood for these classic stories and draw you into their world. Did I succeed?

LAMB TO THE SLAUGHTER

About the Author

Roald Dahl

Roald Dahl wrote two novels, six movie scripts and a number of short stories for adults, but he is probably most famous for his children's stories.

Born: September 13, 1916, in Wales, Great Britain

Quote: "And above all, watch with glittering eyes the whole world around you because the greatest secrets are always hidden in the most unlikely places."

More about Roald Dahl

- At age 23, he became a pilot with the Royal Air Force and fought in World War II.
- He was injured during battle and, in 1942, was sent to Washington, D.C., as an air attaché (a pilot who takes part in a diplomatic mission).
- While in Washington, he met C. S. Forrester, author of *The African Queen*, who encouraged Dahl to write.
- His first real commercial success was *James and the Giant Peach*, published in 1961.
- He declared that, without his own children, it would have been impossible for him to have written children's books.

The short story you'll be reading, "Lamb to the Slaughter," can be found in the book Lamb to the Slaughter and Other Stories. It demonstrates Dahl's belief that "What's horrible is basically funny. In fiction."

Awards include:

- Mystery Writers of America Award (1954, 1959, 1980)
- New York Times Outstanding Books Award (1983)
- Good Book Guide "Best Books of the Past 20 Years" (1997)
- Millennium Children's Book Award (2000)

Works include:

- *The BFG*
- *Charlie and the Chocolate Factory*
- *Charlie and the Great Glass Elevator*
- *The Complete Adventures of Charlie and Mr. Willie Wonka*
- *The Enormous Crocodile*
- *The Gremlins*
- *James and the Giant Peach*
- *Matilda*
- *The Twits*

- *The Witches*
- *Sometime Never*
- *A Piece of Cake*
- *Georgy Porgy*
- *Katina*
- *Man From the South*
- *Pig*
- *Royal Jelly*
- *Skin*
- *Someone Like You*
- *Lamb to the Slaughter and Other Stories*

Story Set-Up ...

In Chapter 1, you read, discussed and wrote about issues dealing with privacy in society. In this story, we deal with things that happen in the privacy of someone's home. Events are set into motion when the husband reveals something private to his wife, with catastrophic results. The police become involved, but do they see what's really going on?

Now ... to the Story!

A Before Reading

ACTIVITY 1

> Associate the following words from the story with an appropriate meaning:

a) blissful (adj.)

b) shame (n.)

c) dazed (adj.)

d) peculiar (adj.)

e) grief (n.)

f) corpse (n.)

g) weapon (n.)

h) weary (adj.)

i) a blow (n.)

j) giggle (v.)

i.   silly or nervous laugh

ii.   disgrace

iii.   strange

iv.   dead body

v.   deep sorrow

vi.   a hard hit

vii.   tired

viii. wonderful

ix.   confused

x.   thing used for attack

ACTIVITY 2

> Read the following statements and decide where you stand on a scale of 1 (completely agree) to 5 (completely disagree). Be ready to defend your point of view with your classmates.

Statements:

- There is no such thing as a perfect marriage.
- A perfect murder needs careful planning.
- Equal rights in a marriage is a myth.
- Murderers should receive the death penalty.
- People see what they want to see, not what is real.

ACTIVITY 3

❯❯ The expression "lamb* to the slaughter**" is something you might say about a gentle person who is unaware that he or she is moving towards disaster. Keeping this in mind, what do you think the short story "Lamb to the Slaughter" will be about?

*A lamb is a young sheep and is often a symbol of innocence.

**Slaughter is killing animals for meat (or killing humans in a vicious manner).

ℬ During Reading

❯❯ Remember to use the RAP strategy as you read. Write down any observations and questions you might have about the events.

❯❯ As you read, fill in a character map for each of the three main characters: Mary Maloney, Patrick Maloney and Detective Noonan.

Example of a character map:

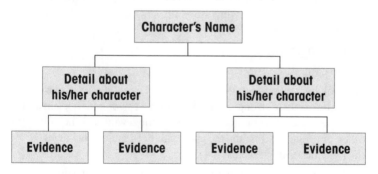

LAMB TO THE SLAUGHTER*

By Roald Dahl

The room was warm and clean, the curtains **drawn**, the two table lamps alight—hers and the one by the empty chair opposite. On the sideboard behind her, two tall glasses, soda water, whiskey. Fresh ice cubes in the Thermos bucket.

005> Mary Maloney was waiting for her husband to come home from work.

Now and again she would glance up at the clock, but without anxiety, merely to please herself with the thought that each minute gone by made it nearer the time when he would come. There was a slow smiling air about her and about everything she did. The drop of a head as she

010> bent over her sewing was curiously tranquil. Her skin—for this was her sixth month **with child**—had acquired a wonderful translucent quality, the mouth was soft, and the eyes, with their new placid look, seemed larger and darker than before. When the clock said ten minutes to five, she began to listen, and a few moments later, punctually as

015> always, she heard the tires on the **gravel** outside, and the car door slamming, the footsteps passing the window, the key turning in the lock. She laid aside her sewing, stood up, and went forward to kiss him as he came in.

"Hullo darling," she said.

020> "Hullo darling," he answered.

She took his coat and hung it in the closet. Then she walked over and made the drinks, a strongish one for him, a weak one for herself; and soon she was back again in her chair with the sewing, and he in the other, opposite, holding the tall glass with both hands, rocking it so

025> the ice cubes **tinkled** against the side.

For her, this was always a **blissful** time of day. She knew he didn't want to speak much until the first drink was finished, and she, on her side, was content to sit quietly, enjoying his company after the long hours alone in the house. She loved to luxuriate in the presence of this man,

030> and to feel—almost as a sunbather feels the sun—that warm male glow that came out of him to her when they were alone together. She loved him for the way he sat loosely in a chair, for the way he came in a door, or moved slowly across the room with long strides. She loved the intent, faraway look in his eyes when they rested on her, the funny
035> shape of the mouth, and especially the way he remained silent about his tiredness, sitting still with himself until the whiskey had taken some of it away.

"Tired darling?"

"Yes," he said. "I'm tired." And as he spoke, he did an unusual thing.
040> He lifted his glass and drained it in one *swallow*, although there was still half of it, at least half of it left. She wasn't really watching him, but she knew what he had done because she heard the ice cubes falling back against the bottom of the empty glass when he lowered his arm. He paused a moment, leaning forward in the chair, then he got up and
045> went slowly over to fetch himself another.

"I'll get it!" she cried, jumping up.

"Sit down," he said.

When he came back, she noticed that the new drink was dark amber with the quantity of whiskey in it.

050> "Darling, shall I get your slippers?"

"No."

She watched him as he began to sip the dark, yellow drink, and she could see little oily swirls in the liquid because
055> it was so strong.

"I think it's a *shame*," she said, "that when a policeman gets to be as senior as you, they keep him walking about on his feet all day long."

Glossary

drawn: shut
with child: pregnant
gravel: small stones
tinkled: made a series of light ringing sounds
blissful: wonderful
swallow: allow food, etc. to pass down the throat
shame: disgrace

060> He didn't answer, so she bent her head again and went on with her sewing; but each time he lifted the drink to his lips, she heard the ice cubes clinking against the side of the glass.

"Darling," she said. "Would you like me to get you some cheese? I haven't made any supper because it's Thursday."

065> "No," he said.

"If you're too tired to eat out," she went on, "it's still not too late. There's plenty of meat and stuff in the freezer, and you can have it right here and not even move out of the chair."

Her eyes waited on him for an answer, a smile, a little nod, but he *070>* made no sign.

"Anyway," she went on, "I'll get you some cheese and crackers first."

"I don't want it," he said.

She moved uneasily in her chair, the large eyes still watching his face. "But you must eat! I'll fix it anyway, and then you can have it or not, *075>* as you like."

She stood up and placed her sewing on the table by the lamp.

"Sit down," he said. "Just for a minute, sit down."

It wasn't till then that she began to get frightened.

"Go on," he said. "Sit down."

080> She lowered herself back slowly into the chair, watching him all the time with those large, **bewildered** eyes. He had finished the second drink and was staring down into the glass, frowning.

"Listen," he said. "I've got something to tell you."

"What is it, darling? What's the matter?"

085> He had now become absolutely motionless, and he kept his head down, so that the light from the lamp beside him fell across the upper part of his face, leaving the chin and mouth in **shadow**. She noticed there was a little muscle moving near the corner of his left eye.

"This is going to be a bit of a shock to you, I'm afraid," he said. "But
090> I've thought about it *a good deal* and I've decided the only thing
to do is tell you right away. I hope you won't blame me too much."

And he told her. It didn't take long, four or five minutes at most,
and she sat very still through it all, watching him with a kind of *dazed*
horror as he went further and further away from her with each word.

095> "So there it is," he added. "And I know it's kind of a bad time to be
telling you, but there simply wasn't any other way. Of course I'll give
you money and see you're looked after. But there needn't really be any
fuss. I hope not anyway. It wouldn't be very good for my job."

Her first instinct was not to believe any of it, to reject it all. It occurred
100> to her that perhaps he hadn't even spoken, that she herself had imagined
the whole thing. Maybe, if she went about her business and acted as
though she hadn't been listening, then later, when she sort of woke
up again, she might find none of it had ever happened.

"I'll get the supper," she managed to whisper, and this time he didn't
105> stop her.

When she walked across the room, she couldn't feel her feet touching
the floor. She couldn't feel anything at all—except a slight nausea and
a desire to vomit. Everything was automatic now—down the steps to
the *cellar*, the light switch, the *deep freeze*, the hand inside the cabinet
110> taking hold of the first object it met.
She lifted it out, and looked at it. It was
wrapped in paper, so she took off the
paper and looked at it again.

A leg of lamb.

115> All right then, they would have lamb
for supper. She carried it upstairs,
holding the thin bone-end of it with
both her hands, and as she went
through the living room, she saw
120> him standing over by the window
with his back to her, and she stopped.

Glossary

bewildered: very confused
shadow: an area that is low in light
a good deal: a lot
dazed: stunned; confused
fuss: commotion; noisy disturbance
cellar: basement
deep freeze: freezer
wrapped: enveloped

"For God's sake," he said, hearing her, but not turning round. "Don't make supper for me. I'm going out."

125> At that point, Mary Maloney simply walked up behind him and, without any pause, she swung the big frozen leg of lamb high in the air and brought it down as hard as she could on the back of his head.

She might just as well have hit him with a steel *club*.

130> She stepped back a pace, waiting, and the funny thing was that he remained standing there for at least four or five seconds, gently swaying. Then he crashed to the carpet.

The violence of the crash, the noise, the small table overturning, helped bring her out of her shock. She came out slowly, feeling cold and surprised, and she stood for a while blinking at the body, still

135> holding the ridiculous piece of meat tight with both hands.

All right, she told herself. So I've killed him.

It was extraordinary, now, how clear her mind became all of a sudden. She began thinking very fast. As the wife of a detective, she knew quite well what the penalty would be. That was fine. It made no difference

140> to her. In fact, it would be a relief. On the other hand, what about the child? What were the laws about murderers with unborn children? Did they kill them both—mother and child? Or did they wait until the tenth month? What did they do?

Mary Maloney didn't know. And she certainly wasn't prepared
145> to take a chance.

She carried the meat into the kitchen, placed it in a pan, turned the oven on high, and *shoved* it inside. Then she washed her hands and ran upstairs to the bedroom. She sat down before the mirror, tidied her hair, *touched up* her lips and face. She tried a smile. It came out
150> rather *peculiar*. She tried again.

"Hullo Sam," she said brightly, aloud.

The voice sounded peculiar too.

"I want some potatoes please, Sam. Yes, and I think a can of peas."

That was better. Both the smile and the voice were coming out better
155> now. She *rehearsed* it several times more. Then she ran downstairs, took her coat, went out the back door, down the garden, into the street.

It wasn't six o'clock yet and the lights were still on in the grocery shop.

"Hullo Sam," she said brightly, smiling at the man behind the counter.

"Why, good evening, Mrs. Maloney. How're you?"

160> "I want some potatoes please, Sam. Yes, and I think a can of peas."

The man turned and reached up behind him on the shelf for the peas.

"Patrick's decided he's tired and doesn't want to eat out tonight," she told him. "We usually go out Thursdays, you know, and now he's caught me without any vegetables in the house."

165> "Then how about meat, Mrs. Maloney?"

"No, I've got meat, thanks. I got a nice leg of lamb from the freezer."

"Oh."

"I don't know much about cooking it frozen, Sam, but I'm taking a chance on
170> it this time. You think it'll be all right?"

"Personally," the grocer said, "I don't believe it makes any difference. You want these Idaho potatoes?"

Glossary

club: bat; heavy stick
shoved: pushed
touched up: freshened
peculiar: strange
rehearsed: repeated

"Oh yes, that'll be fine. Two of those."

175> "Anything else?" The grocer cocked his head on one side, looking at her pleasantly. "How about afterwards? What you going to give him for afterwards?"

"Well—what would you suggest, Sam?"

The man glanced around his shop. "How about a nice big slice
180> of cheesecake? I know he likes that."

"Perfect," she said. "He loves it."

And when it was all wrapped and she had paid, she put on her brightest smile and said, "Thank you, Sam. Goodnight."

"Goodnight, Mrs. Maloney. And thank you."

185> And now, she told herself as she hurried back, all she was doing now, she was returning home to her husband and he was waiting for his supper; and she must cook it well, and make it as **tasty** as possible because the poor man was tired; and if, when she entered the house, she happened to find anything unusual, or tragic, or terrible, then
190> naturally it would be a shock and she'd become frantic with **grief** and horror. Mind you, she wasn't expecting to find anything. She was just going home with the vegetables. Mrs. Patrick Maloney going home with the vegetables on Thursday evening to cook supper for her husband.

195> That's the way, she told herself. Do everything right and natural. Keep things absolutely natural and there'll be no need for any acting at all.

Therefore, when she entered the kitchen by the back door, she was **humming** a little tune to herself and smiling.

"Patrick!" she called. "How are you, darling?"

200> She put the **parcel** down on the table and went through into the living room; and when she saw him lying there on the floor with his legs doubled up and one arm twisted back underneath his body, it really was rather a shock. All the old love and longing for him **welled up** inside her, and she ran over to him, knelt down beside him, and
205> began to cry her heart out. It was easy. No acting was necessary.

A few minutes later, she got up and went to the phone. She knew the number of the police station, and when the man at the other end answered, she cried to him, "Quick! Come quick! Patrick's dead!"

"Who's speaking?"

210> "Mrs. Maloney. Mrs. Patrick Maloney."

"You mean Patrick Maloney's dead?"

"I think so," she sobbed. "He's lying on the floor and I think he's dead."

"Be right over," the man said.

The car came very quickly, and when she opened the front door, two
215> policemen walked in. She know them both—she knew nearly all the men at that ***precinct***—and she fell right into a chair, then went over to join the other one, who was called O'Malley, kneeling by the body.

"Is he dead?" she cried.

"I'm afraid he is. What happened?"

220> Briefly, she told her story about going out to the grocer and coming back to find him on the floor. While she was talking, crying and talking, Noonan discovered a small patch of congealed blood on the dead man's head. He showed it to O'Malley who got up at once and hurried to the phone.

225> Soon, other men began to come into the house. First a doctor, then two detectives, one of whom she knew by name. Later, a police photographer arrived and took pictures, and a man
230> who knew about fingerprints. There was a great deal of whispering and muttering beside the ***corpse***, and the detectives kept asking her a lot of questions. But they always ***treated***
235> her kindly. She told her story again, this time right from the beginning, when Patrick had come in, and she

Glossary

tasty: delicious
grief: deep sorrow; misery
humming: singing without saying words and with closed lips
parcel: package
welled up: filled with emotion
precinct: police office for an area
corpse: dead body
treated: dealt with

was sewing, and he was tired, so tired he hadn't wanted to go out for supper. She told how she'd put the meat in the oven—"it's there now,
240> cooking"—and how she'd stepped out to the grocer for vegetables, and come back to find him lying on the floor.

"Which grocer?" one of the detectives asked.

She told him, and he turned and whispered something to the other detective, who immediately went outside into the street.

245> In fifteen minutes, he was back with a page of notes, and there was more whispering, and through her *sobbing* she heard a few of the whispered phrases— ... "acted quite normal ... very cheerful ... wanted to give him a good supper ... peas ... cheesecake ... impossible that she ..."

After a while, the photographer and the doctor departed and two
250> other men came in and took the corpse away on a *stretcher*. Then the fingerprint man went away. The two detectives remained and so did the two policemen. They were exceptionally nice to her, and Jack Noonan asked if she wouldn't rather go somewhere else, to her sister's house perhaps, or to his own wife, who would take care of her and
255> *put her up* for the night.

No, she said. She didn't feel she could move even a yard at the moment. Would they mind awfully if she stayed just where she was until she felt better. She didn't feel too good at the moment, she really didn't.

Then hadn't she better lie down on the bed? Jack Noonan asked.

260> No, she said. She'd like to stay right where she was, in this chair. A little later, perhaps, when she felt better, she would move.

So they left her there while they went about their business, searching the house. Occasionally one of the detectives asked her another question. Sometimes Jack Noonan spoke at her gently as he passed
265> by. Her husband, he told her, had been killed by *a blow* on the back of the head administered with a heavy *blunt* instrument, almost certainly a large piece of metal. They were looking for the *weapon*. The murderer may have taken it with him, but on the other hand he may have thrown it away or hidden it somewhere on the *premises*.

270> "It's the old story," he said. "Get the weapon, and you've got the man."

Later, one of the detectives came up and sat beside her. Did she know, he asked, of anything in the house that could've been used as the weapon? Would she mind having a look around to see if anything was missing—a very big *spanner*, for example, or a heavy metal vase.

275> They didn't have any heavy metal vases, she said.

"Or a big spanner?"

She didn't think they had a big spanner. But there might be some things like that in the garage.

The search went on. She knew that there were other policemen
280> in the garden all around the house. She could hear their footsteps on the gravel outside, and sometimes she saw a flash of a *torch* through a *chink* in the curtains. It began to get late, nearly nine, she noticed by the clock on the mantle. The four men searching the rooms seemed to be growing *weary*, a trifle exasperated.

285> "Jack," she said, the next time Sergeant Noonan went by. "Would you mind giving me a drink?"

"Sure I'll give you a drink. You mean this whiskey?"

290> "Yes please. But just a small one. It might make me feel better."

He handed her the glass.

"Why don't you have one yourself," she said. "You must be awfully tired. Please
295> do. You've been very good to me."

"Well," he answered. "It's not strictly allowed, but I might take just a drop to keep me going."

One by one, the others came in and
300> were persuaded to take a little nip

Glossary

sobbing: crying, while breathing in gasps
stretcher: a portable bed for carrying sick, injured or dead people
put her up: let her stay
a blow: a knock; a hit
blunt: round; not sharp
weapon: object used for attack
premises: grounds; site
spanner: wrench, a tool for turning nuts and bolts
torch: flashlight
chink: gap; crack
weary: tired

of whiskey. They stood around rather awkwardly with the drinks in their hands, uncomfortable in her presence, trying to say consoling things to her. Sergeant Noonan wandered into the kitchen, came out quickly and said, "Look, Mrs. Maloney. You know that oven of yours is
305> still on, and the meat still inside."

"Oh dear me!" she cried. "So it is!"

"I'd better turn it off for you, hadn't I?"

"Will you do that, Jack. Thank you so much."

When the sergeant returned the second time, she looked at him
310> with her large, dark, tearful eyes. "Jack Noonan," she said.

"Yes?"

"Would you do me a small favour—you and these others?"

"We can try, Mrs. Maloney."

"Well," she said. "Here you all are, and good friends of dear Patrick's
315> too, and helping to catch the man who killed him. You must be terribly hungry by now because it's long past your suppertime, and I know Patrick would never forgive me, God bless his soul, if I allowed you

to remain in his house without offering you decent hospitality. Why don't you eat up that lamb that's in the oven. It'll be cooked 320> just right by now."

"Wouldn't dream of it," Sergeant Noonan said.

"Please," she begged. "Please eat it. Personally I couldn't touch a thing, certainly not what's been in the house when he was here. But it's all right for you. It'd be a favour to me if you'd eat it up. Then you can 325> go on with your work again afterwards."

There was a good deal of hesitating among the four policemen, but they were clearly hungry, and in the end they were persuaded to go into the kitchen and help themselves. The woman stayed where she was, listening to them speaking among themselves, their voices thick 330> and sloppy because their mouths were full of meat.

"Have some more, Charlie?"

"No. Better not finish it."

"She wants us to finish it. She said so. Be doing her a favour."

"Okay then. Give me some more."

335> "That's the hell of a big club the guy must've used to hit poor Patrick," one of them was saying. "The doc says his **skull** was smashed all to pieces just like from a **sledgehammer**."

"That's why it ought to be easy to find."

"Exactly what I say."

340> "Whoever done it, they're not going to be carrying a thing like that around with them longer than they need."

One of them **belched**.

"Personally, I think it's right here 345> on the premises."

"Probably right under our very noses. What you think, Jack?"

And in the other room, Mary Maloney began to **giggle**.

Glossary

skull: head; cranium
sledgehammer: very big hammer
belched: burped
giggle: a silly or nervous laugh

Exploring the Story ...

After Reading

ACTIVITY 1

❯❯ Briefly explain the plot of "Lamb to the Slaughter."

Remember: the plot of a story is the sequence of events.
   The five main elements of plot are:

a) Exposition: the author introduces the character and the setting (time and place).

b) Rising Action: complications begin and the reader feels that something is about to happen.

c) Climax: this is usually the turning point in the story.

d) Falling Action: these are the events that follow the climax.

e) Resolution: this is the outcome of the conflict.

ACTIVITY 2

❯❯ Reread the story to the end of line 103.

a) How would you describe the relationship between Mary and Patrick? Use examples from the story to support your point of view.

b) What is the first clue that tells Mary that Patrick is disturbed about something?

c) The author does not tell us what Patrick revealed to Mary. Why do you think this is so?

d) What do you think Patrick told Mary that shocked her so much?

e) Why does Patrick say to Mary, "And I know it's kind of a bad time to be telling you"?

>> Now reread from lines 104–150.

f) After she hears the news, why does Mary continue to prepare the dinner?

g) Did Mary's subsequent actions surprise you? Why or why not?

>> Continue rereading from lines 151–205.

h) Why does Mary go to the store to buy vegetables?

i) When Mary sees her husband's body on her return from the store, the author says, "… she ran over to him, knelt down beside him, and began to cry her heart out. It was easy. No acting was necessary." Why do you think the author says this?

>> Finally, reread from line 206 to the end of the story.

j) Why do you think that the police eliminate Mary as a murder suspect?

k) What conclusions do the police come to about the murder of Patrick Maloney?

ACTIVITY 3

>> Irony can be described as a situation happening that is very different from what is expected. Explain the irony in the title "Lamb to the Slaughter."

>> Why are the following sentences ironic?

a) "It's the old story," he said. "Get the weapon and you've got the man." (line 270)

b) "It'd be a favour to me if you'd eat it up. Then you can go on with your work again afterwards." (line 324) c) "She wants us to finish it. She said so. Be doing her a favour." (line 333)

d) "Personally, I think it's right here on the premises." "Probably right under our very noses." (line 344)

𝒟 Your Thoughts?

a) How do you feel towards Mary at the end of the story? Have your feelings changed since the beginning?

b) Why do you think Roald Dahl titled this short story "Lamb to the Slaughter"? Who is/are the lamb(s)?

c) Go back now to page 4 and decide whether the author agrees or disagrees with the statements in Before Reading: Activity 2. Be prepared to argue your point of view, using examples from the story.

𝒞 Links to Chapter 1

a) Do you think that couples should always share their most private thoughts with each other? Explain.

b) People often want to control what others think about them. They also often guard their privacy for this reason. How could this explain some of the actions taken by Patrick and Mary? Use examples from the story to support your answer.

I'VE GOT GLORIA

Who is M. E. Kerr? Well, no one, actually! M. E. Kerr is the pen name (pseudonym) for Marijane Meaker, one of today's leading authors of young adult fiction.

Born: May 27, 1927, in Auburn, New York

Quote: "… I remember being depressed by all the neatly tied-up, happy-ending stories, the abundance of winners, the themes of winning, solving, finding—when around me it didn't seem that easy."

More about M. E. Kerr

- Her friend Louise Fitzhugh, author of *Harriet the Spy*, encouraged her to adopt the pen name M. E. Kerr.
- Her other pen names include Mary Jane, Ann Aldrich and Vin Packer. She also publishes in her own name.
- From the time she was a child, she knew she wanted to be a writer.
- Her writing is known for its wit and humour.
- She tackles serious themes like love, prejudice, race, divorce, religion, class differences, and sexuality.
- She writes books for adults and children too.
- The short story you'll be reading, "I've Got Gloria," is part of the 1997 anthology called *No Easy Answers: Short Stories About Teenagers Making Tough Choices*.

Awards include:

- Margaret A. Edwards Award (1993), from the American Library Association for lifetime accomplishments
- National Council of Teachers of English ALAN Award for outstanding contributions to young adult literature

Works include:

- *Blood on My Forehead*
- *Dinky Hocker Shoots Smack!*
- *Fell*
- *Fell Back*
- *Fell Down*
- *Gentlehands*
- *"Hello," I Lied*
- *Him She Loves?*
- *I'll Love You When You're More Like Me*
- *If I Love You, Am I Trapped Forever?*
- *Deliver Us From Evie*
- *Is That You, Miss Blue?*
- *Little Little*
- *Linger*
- *Love Is a Missing Person*
- *Night Kites*
- *Slap Your Sides*
- *Someone Like Summer*
- *The Son of Somebody Famous*
- *What Became of Her*
- *What I Really Think of You*

Story Set-Up ...

In Chapter 2, you examined the question of normal behaviour in young people. You learned that, while some behaviours are perfectly normal, they are not necessarily desirable. The story you are about to read deals with this same issue. Scott, the "hero" of the story, grapples with a problem and finds an unusual way to solve it. You will quickly decide if this solution is normal or not.

Now ... to the Story!

𝒜 Before Reading

ACTIVITY 1

❱ Match the following words from the story with an appropriate meaning:

a) anxious (adj.)   i.   must

b) deal (n.)   ii.   twenty-five cents

c) have to (v.)   iii. feeling nervous

d) hothead (n.)   iv.   desires

e) speak up (v.)   v.   arrangement

f) a quarter (n.)   vi.   temperamental

g) wishes (n.)   vii. talk louder

ACTIVITY 2

❱ Predict the answers to these questions by reading the following quotes from the short story:

Questions:

a) Who is telling the story?

b) Who is Gloria?

c) Who is Mrs. Whitman?

d) What do you think the story is about?

Quotes:

From the **beginning** of the story:

"Hello? Mrs. Whitman?"
"Yes?"
"I've got Gloria."

From the **middle** of the story:

"Mrs. Whitman? I don't mean to be hard on you, but that's the deal, see. A thou in hundreds."
"Just don't hurt Gloria."

From **near the end** of the story:

"I didn't know Mrs. Whitman's number. I'd copied it down from one of the Lost Dog signs, and ripped it up after I'd called her."

From the **end** of the story:

"This is Martha Whitman. Tell him I'll see him this summer. I'm teaching remedial math."

B During Reading

❯ First, <u>skim</u> the story quickly to check your answers to the previous activity.

❯ Then <u>reread</u> the story <u>slowly</u>. Make a model of a reading log and fill in the columns.

Example of a reading log:

Main events in story	Your personal reflections or questions
Scott called Mrs. Whitman to say he had Gloria.	Scott seems to be very impulsive and upset.

I'VE GOT GLORIA

By M. E. Kerr

"Hello? Mrs. Whitman?"

"Yes?"

"I've got Gloria."

"Oh, thank heaven! Is she all right?"

005> "She's fine, Mrs. Whitman."

"Where is she?"

"She's here with me."

"Who are you?"

"You can call me Bud."

010> "Bud who?"

"Never mind that, Mrs. Whitman. I've got your little dog and she's anxious to get back home."

"Oh, I know she is. She must miss me terribly. Where are you? I'll come and get her right away."

015> "Not so fast, Mrs. Whitman. First, there's a little something you must do."

"Anything. Just tell me where to find you."

"I'll find you, Mrs. Whitman, after you do as I say."

"What do you mean, Bud?"

"I mean that I'll need some money before I get Gloria home safely to you."

020> "Money?"

"She's a very valuable dog."

"Not really. I got her from the ***pound***."

"But she's valuable to you, isn't she?"

"She's everything to me."

025> "So you have to prove it, Mrs. Whitman."

"What is this?"

"A dognapping. I have your dog and you have to pay to have her returned safely to you."

There was a pause.

030> I could just imagine her face—that face I have hated ever since she **flunked** me. That mean, freckled face, with the glasses over those hard, little green eyes, the small, **pursed** lips, the mop of frizzy red hair topping it all … Well, top this, Mrs. Whitman: I do not even have that **nutsy** little bulldog of yours. She is lost, just as your countless signs nailed
035> up everywhere announce that she is … All I have is this one chance to get revenge, and I'm grabbing it!

Now her voice came carefully, "How much do you want?"

"A thousand dollars, Mrs. Whitman. A thou, in one-hundred-dollar bills, and Gloria will be back drooling on your lap."

040> "A thousand dollars?"

Got to you, didn't I? Did your stomach turn over the way mine did when I saw that F in math?

"You heard me, Mrs. Whitman."

"Are you one of my students?"

045> "Oh, like I'm going to tell you if I am."

"You must be."

"I could be, couldn't I? You're not everyone's dream teacher, are you?"

"Please don't hurt my dog."

050> "I'm not cruel by nature."

I don't **take after** my **old man.** He said he was sorry that I flunked math because he knew how much I was counting on the hike through
055> Yellowstone this summer. He said

Glossary

pound: a place for abandoned animals
flunked: failed
pursed: pressed tightly together (usually lips)
nutsy: crazy; silly
take after: resemble someone in behaviour or looks
old man: a disrespectful name for an older man, often one's father

maybe the other guys would take some photographs, so I could see what I was missing while I went to summer school to get a passing grade. "Gee, Scott," he said, "what a shame, and now you won't get an allowance either or have TV in your bedroom or the use of the

060> computer. But never mind, **sonny boy**," he said, "there'll be lots to do around the house. I'll leave lists for you every day of things to be done before I get home."

Mrs. Whitman **whined**, "I just don't have a thousand dollars. I don' know where I'll get so much money, either."

065> Sometimes I whined that way, and my mom would say, "Scotty, we wouldn't be so hard on you if you'd only take responsibility for your actions. We tell you to be in at eleven p.m. and you claim the bus was late. We ask you to take the tapes back to Videoland, and you say we never said to do it. You always have an excuse for everything! You never

070> blame yourself!"

"Mrs. Whitman? I don't mean to be hard on you, but that's the deal, see. A thou in hundreds."

"Just don't hurt Gloria."

"Gee, what a shame that you have to worry about such a thing. She's

075> a sweet little dog, and I know she misses you because she's not eating."

"She doesn't eat dog food, Bud. I cook for her."

"That's why she doesn't eat, hmm? I don't know how to cook."

"You could just put a frozen dinner in the microwave. A turkey dinner or a Swanson's pot roast. I'll pay you for it."

080> "A thousand dollars plus ten for frozen dinners? Is that what you're suggesting?"

"Let me think. Please. I have to think how I can get the money."

"Of course you do. I'll call you back, Mrs. Whitman, and meanwhile I'll go to the store and get some Swanson's frozen dinners."

085> "When will you—"

I hung up.

I could hear Dad coming
up the stairs.

"Scott?"

090> "Yes, sir?"

"I'm going to take the Saturn in for an oil
change. I want you to come with me."

"I have some homework, sir."

"I want you to come with me. Now."

095> In the car, he said, "We need to talk."

"About what?" I said.

There was one of her Lost Dog signs tacked
to the telephone pole at the end of our street.

"We need to talk about this summer," he said.

100> "What about it?"

"You have to make up the math grade.
That you have to do. I'm sorry you can't
go to Yellowstone."

"Yeah."

105> "There's no other way if you want to
get into any kind of college. Your other
grades are fine. But you need math ...
What's so hard about math, Scott?"

Glossary

sonny boy: a patronizing
name for someone who is
younger than the person
who is speaking

whined: complained in
a childish way

"I hate it!"

110> "I did, too, but I learned it. You have to study."

"Mrs. Whitman doesn't like me."

"Why doesn't she like you?"

"She doesn't like anyone but that bulldog."

"Who's lost, apparently."

115> "Yeah."

"The signs are everywhere."

"Yeah."

"But she wouldn't deliberately flunk you, would she?"

"Who knows?"

120> "Do you really think a teacher would flunk you because she doesn't like you?"

"Who knows?"

"Scott, you've got to admit when you're wrong. I'll give you an example. I was wrong when I said you couldn't have an allowance or TV or use
125> the computer, et cetera. I was angry and I just *blew*! That was wrong. It wouldn't have made it any easier for you while you're trying to get a passing grade in math. So I was wrong! I apologize and I *take it back*."

"*How come?*"

"How come? Because I'm sorry. I thought about it and it *bothered* me.
130> I'm a hothead, and I don't like that about myself. Okay?"

"Yeah."

"Maybe that's what's wrong here."

"What's wrong where?"

"Between us."

135> "Is something wrong between us?"

"Scotty, I'm trying to talk with you. About us. I want to work things out so we *get along* better."

"Yeah."

"Sometimes I do or say **rash** things."

140> "Yeah."

"I always feel **lousy** after."

"Oh, yeah?"

"Do you understand? I shouldn't take things out on you. That's **petty**. Life is hard enough. We don't have to be mean and **spiteful** with each 145> other. Agreed?"

"Yeah." I was thinking about the time our dog didn't come home one night. I couldn't sleep. I even prayed. When he got back all muddy the next morning, I broke into tears and told him, "Now you're making me **blubber** like a baby!"

150> Dad was still on my case.

"Scott, I want you to think about why Mrs. Whitman flunked you."

"I just told you: she doesn't like me."

"Are you really convinced that you're good at math, but the reason you failed was because she doesn't like you?"

155> "Maybe."

"Is she a good teacher?"

"She never smiles. She's got these tight little lips and these ugly **freckles**."

"So she's not a good teacher?"

160> "I can't learn from her."

"Did you study hard?"

"I studied. Sure. I studied."

"How many others flunked math?"

"What?"

165> "How many others flunked math?"

"No one."

Glossary

blow (blew): explode
take it back: retract
how come?: why?
bothered: disturbed; annoyed
get along: be on good terms with someone
rash: reckless; acting without a lot of thought
lousy: bad
petty: trivial, unimportant
spiteful: hurtful; nasty
blubber: cry loudly
freckles: spots on the skin

"Speak up."

"I said, I'm the only one."

"So others learn from her, despite her tight little lips and ugly freckles?"

170> "I guess."

"Scott, who's to blame for your flunking math?"

"Okay," I said. "Okay."

"Who is to blame?"

"Me. Okay? I didn't study that hard."

175> He sighed and said, "There. Good. You've accepted the blame … How do you feel?"

"I feel okay." I really didn't, though. I was thinking about the dumb bulldog running loose somewhere, and about Mrs. Whitman worried sick now that she thought Gloria'd been dognapped.

180> Dad said, "I think we both feel a lot better."

We sat around in the waiting room at Saturn.

Dad read *Sports Illustrated*, but I couldn't concentrate on the magazines there or the ballgame on TV. I was down. I knew what Dad meant when he'd told me he felt bad after he "blew" and that he didn't like

185> himself for it.

I kept glancing toward the pay phone. I stuck my hands in my pants pockets. I had a few quarters.

"I'm going to call Al and see what he's doing tonight," I said.

Dad said, "Wait until you get home. We'll be leaving here very shortly."

190> "I'm going to look around," I said.

I didn't know Mrs. Whitman's number. I'd copied it down from one of the Lost Dog signs and ripped it up after I'd called her. I hadn't planned to follow up the call, get money from her: nothing like that. I just wanted to give her a good scare.

195> I went over to the phone book and looked her up.

Then I ducked inside the phone booth, fed the slot a quarter, and dialled.

"Hello?"

"Mrs. Whitman? I don't have your dog. I was playing a joke."

200> "I know you don't have my dog. Gloria's home. The dog warden found her and brought her back right after you hung up on me."

I was relieved. At least she wouldn't have to go all night worrying about getting Gloria back.

"I was wrong," I said. "It was petty. I'm sorry."

205> "Do you know what you put me through, Scott Perkins?"

I just hung up.

I stood there with my face ***flaming***.

"Scott?" My father was looking all over for me, calling me and calling me. "Scott! Are you here? The car's ready!"

210> All the way home, he lectured me on how contrary I was. Why couldn't I have waited to phone Al? What was it about me that made me just go ahead and do something I was expressly told I shouldn't do? "Just when I think we've gotten someplace," he said, "you turn around and go against my wishes."

215> "Why?" he shouted.

I said, "What?" I hadn't been concentrating on all that he was saying. I was thinking that now she knew my name—don't ask me how— and now what was she going to do about it?

"I asked you why you go against my wishes," Dad said. "Nothing I say
220> seems to register with you."

Glossary

flaming: bright red

"It registers with me." I said. "I just seem to *screw up* sometimes."

"I can hardly believe my ears." He was smiling. "You actually said sometimes you screw up. That's a new one."

"Yeah," I said. "That's a new one."

225> Then we both laughed, but I was still shaking, remembering Mrs. Whitman saying my name that way.

When we got in the house, Mom said, "The funniest thing happened while you were gone. The phone rang and this woman asked what number this was. I told her, and she asked whom she was speaking to.

230> I told her and she said, 'Perkins … Perkins. Do you have a boy named Scott?' I said that we did, and she said, 'This is Martha Whitman. Tell him I'll see him this summer. I'm teaching *remedial* math.'"

I figured that, right after I'd hung up from calling her about Gloria, she'd dialled *69. I'd heard you could do that. The phone would ring

235> whoever called you last. That was why she'd asked my mother what number it was and who was speaking.

Dad said, "You see, Scott. Mrs. Whitman doesn't dislike you, or she wouldn't have called here to tell you she'd see you this

240> summer."

"I was wrong," I said. "Wrong again."

Oh, was I ever!

Glossary

screw up: make a mess of things

remedial: corrective

Exploring the Story ...

𝒞 After Reading

ACTIVITY 1

a) Describe Mrs. Whitman's reaction to Scott's first phone call. Which words or expressions from the story demonstrate this?

b) Describe Scott's attitude during this phone call. Name the words or expressions from the story that demonstrate this.

c) Scott tells Mrs. Whitman that this is a "dognapping." What does he mean by that?

d) Why does Scott want to hurt Mrs. Whitman this way? Which line in the story gave you the answer?

e) In lines 51–62, Scott reflects on how his father reacted when he failed math. What sort of father does he seem to be?

⊗ Reread the story to the end of line 94.

f) How would you describe Scott? Which lines in the story give you that information?

⊗ Now reread Scott's conversation with his father (lines 95–180).

g) What impression do you get of Scott's father now? What new information do you learn about Scott?

⊗ Then reread lines 181–209.

h) What emotion does Scott experience?

i) What surprise does Scott get?

⊗ Finally, reread from line 210 to the end of the story.

j) In your own words, describe what happens in this final part of the story.

ACTIVITY 2

❯ Explain what the underlined expressions mean.

a) "Never mind that Mrs. Whitman." (p. 26)

b) "Well, top this, Mrs. Whitman." (p. 27)

c) "Got to you, didn't I?" (p. 27)

d) "Scotty, we wouldn't be so hard on you if ..." (p. 28)

e) "Dad was still on my case." (p. 31)

f) "I was down." (p. 32)

Your Thoughts?

a) Have you ever felt angry at a teacher? Was your reaction normal or not? Explain.

b) How would you feel and act the first day of summer school if you were Scott?

c) How do you think Mrs. Whitman will behave towards him?

Links to Chapter 2

a) Do you think Scott behaved in a normal way? Explain.

b) Do you think his parents (especially his father) behaved in a normal way? Explain.

c) How do you think Scott can avoid making these types of mistakes in the future? Use what you learned in Chapter 2 to support your opinions.

MY SISTER'S KEEPER

About the Author

Jodi Picoult

What kind of stories does Jodi Picoult write? Stories that talk about family, relationships and the ups and downs of love. They focus on questions and issues that stay with a reader long after the book is finished.

Born: May 19, 1966, in Long Island, New York

Quote: "… I am the world's worst friend. Tell me something and it's likely to end up in a character's mouth … I usually draw a plot out of thin air, but pepper the book with real-life conversations."

More about Jodi Picoult

- She had two short stories published in *Seventeen* magazine while she was still in college.
- Jodi's career path included work as a technical writer, a copywriter at an ad agency, an editor and an 8th grade English teacher.
- Despite her talent, it took years for her to find a literary agent that would represent her.
- She and her husband Tim have three children. They live in New Hampshire, USA.
- Her books have been translated into thirty-four languages.

The story you'll be reading is an excerpt from her 2004 best-selling novel My Sister's Keeper.

Awards include:

- New England Bookseller Award for Fiction (2003)
- Book Browse Diamond Award for novel of the year
- *Cosmopolitan* magazine's "Fearless Fiction" Award (2007)
- Vermont Green Mountain Book Award

Works include:

- *Songs of the Humpback Whale*
- *Harvesting the Heart*
- *Picture Perfect*
- *Mercy*
- *The Pact*
- *Keeping Faith*
- *Plain Truth*
- *Salem Falls*
- *Perfect Match*
- *Second Glance*
- *My Sister's Keeper*
- *Vanishing Acts*
- *The Tenth Circle*
- *Nineteen Minutes*
- *Change of Heart*

Story Set-Up …

In Chapter 3, you examined some of the moral questions that arise because of scientific advances. You learned that, although most of these advances are helpful, they also create problems that don't have easy solutions. The story you are about to read concerns a family that is dealing with a life-threatening illness. Kate, the older daughter, has leukemia. Anna, the younger daughter, is not sick, but she has had many medical procedures in order to help her sister beat leukemia—the disease that threatens her life. As Anna gets older, she wonders about her life and the reason she was born. Does she really have to be her sister's keeper?

Now ... to the Story!

𝒜 Before Reading

ACTIVITY 1

» Associate each of the words below with an antonym in Word Bank 1. These words will help you understand the story better.

a) cheap

b) truth

c) healthy

d) cling to

e) hurt

f) sunset

g) pitch

h) sell

i) roar

WORD Bank 1

catch	buy	whisper
lie	abandon	expensive
help	sick	sunrise

ACTIVITY 2

» Associate each of the words below with a synonym in Word Bank 2. These words will help you understand the story better.

a) junk

b) teddy bear

c) naked

d) spill

e) fade

f) guess

g) provide

h) collapse

WORD Bank 2

give	type of stuffed animal
nude	flow out / fall out
garbage	suppose
fall apart	disappear slowly

ACTIVITY 3

» Read the following information about leukemia and the treatment that can help Anna's sister, Kate. Do you know anyone who has suffered a life-threatening illness like leukemia?

What is leukemia?

Leukemia is a cancer of the blood and bone marrow. It affects more children than any other type of cancer. One type of treatment is a bone marrow transplant. This requires a bone marrow donor—someone who is a genetic match. It is not easy to find a donor match. In general, people hesitate to donate bone marrow, since the procedure involves inserting a needle into a donor's large bone. The donor is put to sleep by general anesthesia during this procedure.

B During Reading

The author uses similes to help you see something in a new way. Similes compare different things, using the words "like" and "as."

Examples: The paint was red like blood.
He was as angry as a bear without food.

» Make a model of a chart below and look for three more similes in the story.

Simile chart:

Sentence	Line #
You know how most little kids think they're like cartoon characters ...	75

MY SISTER'S KEEPER

By Jodi Picoult

I was born for a very specific purpose. I wasn't the result of a cheap bottle of wine or a full moon or the heat of the moment. I was born because a scientist managed to **hook up** my mother's eggs and my father's sperm to create a specific combination of precious genetic
005> material. In fact, when Jesse told me how babies get made and I, the great **disbeliever**, decided to ask my parents the truth, I got more than I **bargained for**. They sat me down and told me all the usual stuff, of course—but they also explained that they chose little embryonic me, specifically, because I could save my sister, Kate. "We loved you even
010> more," my mother made sure to say, "because we knew what exactly we were getting."

It made me wonder, though, what would have happened if Kate had been healthy. Chances are, I'd still be floating up in Heaven or wherever, waiting to be attached to a body to spend some time
015> on Earth. Certainly I would not be part of this family. See, unlike the rest of the free world, I didn't get here by accident. And if your parents have you for a reason, then that reason better exist. Because once it's gone, so are you.

Pawnshops may be full of junk, but they're also a **breeding ground**
020> for stories, if you ask me—not that you did. What happened to make
a person trade in the Never Before Worn Diamond Solitaire? Who
needed money so badly they'd sell a teddy bear missing an eye? As
I walk up to the counter, I wonder if someone will look at the **locket**
I'm about to give up, and ask these same questions.

025> The man at the cash register has a nose the shape of a **turnip** and eyes
sunk so deep, I can't imagine how he sees well enough to go about his
business. "Need something?" he asks.

It's all I can do to not turn around and
walk out the door, pretend I've come in
030> by mistake. The only thing that keeps
me **steady** is knowing I am not the first
person to stand in front of this counter
holding the one item in the world
I never thought I'd **part with**.

035> "I have something to sell," I tell him.

"Am I supposed to guess what it is?"

"Oh." Swallowing, I pull the locket out
of the pocket of my jeans. The heart
falls on the glass counter in a pool of its
040> own chain. "It's fourteen-karat gold,"
I pitch. "Hardly ever worn." This is a lie;
until this morning, I haven't taken it off
in seven years. My father gave it to me
when I was 6, after the **bone marrow**
045> **harvest**, because he said anyone who
was giving her sister such a major
present deserved one of her own.
Seeing it there, on the counter, my
neck feels shivery and naked.

Glossary

hook up: connect
disbeliever: someone
who doesn't believe
bargained for: expected
pawnshops: places where
you trade personal objects
for money
breeding ground: a place
where specific things
grow well
locket: small piece
of jewellery that can
hold a small object
or photo inside it
turnip: yellow root
vegetable
steady: secure
part with: give away
bone marrow harvest:
collecting tissue from
inside bones
(for medical reasons)

050> The owner puts a loop up to his eye, which makes it seem almost normal size. "I'll give you twenty."

"Dollars?"

"No, pesos. What did you think?"

"It's worth five times that!" I'm guessing.

055> The owner shrugs. "I'm not the one who needs the money."

I pick up the locket, ***resigned*** to ***sealing the deal***, and the strangest thing happens—my hand, it just clamps shut like the ***Jaws of Life***. My face goes red with the effort to peel apart my fingers. It takes what seems like an hour for that locket to spill into the owner's

060> ***outstretched*** palm. His eyes stay on my face, softer now. "Tell them you lost it," he offers, advice tossed in for free.

If Mr. Webster had decided to put the word "***freak***" in his dictionary, Anna Fitzgerald would be the best definition he could give. It's more than just the way I look: ***refugee***-skinny with absolutely no chest to

065> speak of, hair the color of dirt, connect-the-dot ***freckles*** on my cheeks that, let me tell you, do not fade with lemon juice or sunscreen or even, sadly, sandpaper. No, God was obviously in some kind of mood on my birthday, because he added to this fabulous physical combination the bigger picture—the ***household*** into which I was born.

070> My parents tried to make things normal, but that's a relative term. The truth is, I was never really a kid. To be honest, neither were Kate and Jesse. I guess maybe my brother had his ***moment in the sun*** for the four years he was alive before Kate got diagnosed, but ever since then, we've been too busy looking over our shoulders to run ***headlong*** into

075> growing up. You know how most little kids think they're like cartoon characters—if an ***anvil*** drops on their heads, they can peel themselves off the sidewalk and keep going? Well, I never once believed that. How could I, when we practically set a place for Death at the dinner table?

Kate has acute ***promyelocytic leukemia***. Actually, that's not quite
080> true—right now she doesn't have it, but it's ***hibernating*** under her
skin like a bear, until it decides to roar again. She was diagnosed
when she was 2; she's 16 now. Molecular relapse and granulocyte and
portacath—these words are part of my vocabulary, even though I'll
never find them on any ***SAT***. I'm an allogeneic donor—a perfect sibling
085> match. When Kate needs leukocytes or stem cells or bone marrow
to ***fool*** her body into thinking it's healthy, I'm the one who provides
them. Nearly every time Kate's hospitalized, I wind up there, too.

None of which means anything, except that you shouldn't believe
what you hear about me, least of all that which I tell you myself.

090> As I am coming up the stairs, my mother comes out of her room
wearing another ***ball gown***. "Ah," she says, turning her back to me.
"Just the girl I wanted to see."

I zip it up and watch her ***twirl***. My mother could be beautiful, if she
were parachuted into someone else's life. She has long dark hair and the
095> fine collarbones of a princess, but the corners of her mouth turn down,
like she's swallowed ***bitter*** news. She doesn't have much free time, since

---

Glossary

resigned: reluctantly agree to
sealing the deal: come to an agreement
Jaws of Life: metal device used to extract people trapped in severely damaged cars
outstretched: open and extended
freak: abnormal person
refugee: person who can no longer live in his/her homeland, due to persecution, war or natural disaster
freckles: brownish spots on the skin
household: members living in a house; family members

moment in the sun: time to feel special
headlong: straight ahead
anvil: heavy iron block
promyelocytic leukemia: type of cancer
hibernating: inactive
SAT: admission test for college in the USA
fool: trick
ball gown: fancy dress
twirl: rotate rapidly
bitter: bad tasting

a calendar is something that can change drastically if my sister develops a bruise or a *nosebleed*, but what she does have she spends at Bluefly.com, ordering ridiculously fancy evening dresses for places she is never going
100> to go. "What do you think?" she asks.

The gown is all the colors of a sunset, and made out of material that swishes when she moves. It's strapless, what a star might wear *sashaying* down a red carpet—totally not the dress code for a *suburban* house in Upper Darby, Rhode Island. My mother twists her hair into a knot and
105> holds it in place. On her bed are three other dresses—one slinky and black, one bugle-beaded, one that seems impossibly small. "You look ..."

Tired. The word bubbles right under my lips.

My mother goes perfectly still, and I wonder if I've said it without meaning to. She holds up a hand, *shushing* me, her ear cocked
110> to the open doorway. "Did you hear that?"

"Hear what?"

"Kate."

"I didn't hear anything."

But she doesn't take my word for it, because when it comes to Kate
115> she doesn't take anybody's word for it. She marches upstairs and opens up our bedroom door to find my sister hysterical on her bed, and just like that the world collapses again. My father, a *closet astronomer*, has tried to explain black holes to me, how they are so heavy they absorb everything, even light, right into their center. Moments like this are
120> the same kind of vacuum; no matter what you cling to, you wind up being *sucked in*.

"Kate!" My mother sinks down to the floor, that stupid skirt a cloud around her.

"Kate, honey, what hurts?"

125> Kate hugs a pillow to her stomach, and tears keep streaming down her face. Her pale hair is stuck to her face in damp streaks; her breathing's too tight. I stand frozen in the doorway of my own room, waiting for instructions: *Call Daddy. Call 911. Call Dr. Chance.* My mother goes so

far as to shake a better explanation out of Kate. "It's Preston," she *sobs*.
130> "He's leaving Serena for good." That's when we notice the TV. On the screen, a blond hottie gives a longing look to a woman crying almost as hard as my sister, and then he slams the door. "But what hurts?" my mother asks, certain there has to be more to it than this.

"Oh my God," Kate says, sniffling. "Do you have any idea how much
135> Serena and Preston *have been through*? Do you?" That *fist* inside me relaxes, now that I know it's all right. Normal, in our house, is like a blanket too short for a bed—sometimes it covers you just fine, and other times it leaves you cold and shaking; and worst of all, you never know which of the two it's going to be.

Glossary

nosebleed: blood coming from the nose
sashaying: moving side to side
suburban: residential area in outlying part of city
shushing: sound made to demand silence
closet astronomer: studies astronomy in private
sucked in: taken by force
sobs: cries, while breathing in gasps
have been through: have faced difficulties
fist: hand closed tightly with fingers in palm

140> I sit down on the end of Kate's bed. Although I'm only 13, I'm taller than her, and every now and then people mistakenly assume I'm the older sister. At different times this summer, she has been crazy for Callahan, Wyatt, and Liam, the male **leads** on this **soap**. Now, I guess, it's all about Preston. "There was the kidnapping scare," I volunteer.

145> I actually followed that story line; Kate made me tape the show during her **dialysis** sessions.

"And the time she almost married his twin by mistake," Kate adds.

"Don't forget when he died in the boat accident. For two months, anyway." My mother joins the conversation, and I remember that *150>* she used to watch this soap, too, sitting with Kate in the hospital.

For the first time, Kate seems to notice my mother's outfit. "What are you wearing?"

"Oh. Something I'm sending back." She stands up in front of me so that I can undo her zipper. This mail-order compulsion, for any other *155>* mother, would be a **wake-up call** for therapy; for my mom, it would probably be considered a healthy break. I wonder if it's putting on someone else's skin for a while that she likes so much, or if it's the option of being able to send back a circumstance that just doesn't **suit** you. She looks at Kate, hard.

160> "You're sure nothing hurts?"

After my mother leaves, Kate **sinks** a little. That's the only way to describe it—how fast color drains from her face, how she disappears against the pillows. As she gets sicker, she fades a little more, until I am afraid one day I will wake up and not be able to see her at all.

165> "Move," Kate orders. "You're blocking the picture."

So I go to sit on my own bed. "It's only the **coming** attractions."

"Well, if I die tonight I want to know what I'm missing."

I fluff my pillows up under my head. Kate, as usual, has **swapped** so that she has all the **funchy** ones that don't feel like rocks under *170>* your neck. She's supposed to deserve this, because she's three years older than me or because she's sick or because the moon is in Aquarius—

there's always a reason. I *squint* at the television, wishing I could flip through the stations, knowing I don't have a prayer. "Preston looks like he's made out of plastic."

175> "Then why did I hear you *whispering* his name last night into your pillow?"

"Shut up," I say.

"You shut up." Then Kate smiles at me. "He probably is gay, though. *Quite a waste*, considering the Fitzgerald sisters are—" Wincing,
180> she breaks off mid-sentence, and I roll towards her.

"Kate?"

She rubs her lower back. "It's nothing."

It's her *kidneys*. "Want me to get Mom?"

"Not yet." She reaches between our
185> beds, which are just far enough apart for us to touch each other if we both try. I hold out my hand, too. When we were little, we'd make this bridge and try to see how many Barbies we could
190> get to balance on it.

Lately, I have been having *nightmares*, where I'm cut into so many pieces that there isn't enough of me to be put back together.

Glossary

leads: main characters
soap: television drama
dialysis: medical procedure to clean kidneys
wake-up call: an alert of negative behaviour
suit: fit
sinks: lowers; drops
coming: future
swapped: switched
funchy: soft and comfortable
squint: eyes partly closed
whispering: speaking in a low voice
quite a waste: not put to good use; too bad (informal)
kidneys: bean-shaped organs that remove waste from the blood and excrete urine
nightmares: bad dreams

Exploring the Story ...

C After Reading

ACTIVITY 1

❯ Read the quotes from the story and answer the questions that follow:

"I was born for a very specific purpose." (line 1)

Who says this line?

What is the specific purpose?

Who helped her be born for this purpose?

"We loved you even more … because we knew exactly what we were getting." (line 9)

Who says this line?

How does this information make Anna feel?

What, exactly, did the speaker know?

"Call Daddy. Call 911. Call Dr. Chance." (line 128)

Who says this line?

Who does she say it to?

Where is she?

ACTIVITY 2

❱❱ Reread the scene at the pawnshop (lines 19–61).

a) Why does Anna go to the pawnshop?

b) Which sentence(s) tell you she is nervous about what she is doing there?

c) When did she receive this object and for what reason?

d) We are not told why she needed the money; can you imagine why she needs it?

❱❱ Continue rereading from lines 62–89.

e) Describe Anna's attitude in her role as her sister's keeper.

f) Why does Anna say that they practically set a place for Death at the dinner table? What is she making a reference to?

g) How long has Kate had leukemia?

h) What does the medical term "allogeneic donor" mean?

❱❱ Now reread the scene with Anna and her mother (lines 90–150).

i) How does Anna describe her mother?

j) What did Anna and her mother think happened when they marched up to Kate's bedroom?

k) Why was Kate crying?

l) What does Anna compare her family's normality to?

❱❱ Finally, reread from line 151 to the end of the story.

m) Find a sentence that shows Anna expressing the following:

• fear

• resentment

• support

𝒟Your Thoughts?

i. Is it morally correct to do whatever it takes to save a child's life, even if means imposing something on another child? (e.g. donating bone marrow or a kidney)

ii. If you were a match and could donate an organ to your sibling, do you think you would do it?

iii. Would you donate an organ to a friend, if you were a match?

iv. When a child has a life-threatening illness, who is it more difficult for: the sick child, the parents or the sibling?

v. How do you think Kate feels about her sister's "helping" role in her life?

𝒞 Links to Chapter 3 ...

i. Do you think science has gone too far in the options it gives people? Explain.

ii. Risky medical procedures, such as organ donation, come with specific rules and guidelines that must be respected, e.g. anonymity, consent, waiting lists. Why do you think these rules are important?

THE DEW BREAKER

Edwidge Danticat

Edwidge Danticat is an American writer born in Haiti. She has written a number of books and documentaries on the plight and trauma of the people in Haiti.

Born: January 19, 1969, near Port-au-Prince, Haiti

Quote: "I wanted to raise the voice of a lot of the people that I knew growing up ... poor people who had extraordinary dreams, but also very amazing obstacles."

More about Edwidge Danticat

- She was brought up by her uncle in Haiti, speaking French and Creole.
- When she was 12 she moved to New York to be with her parents and started to learn English.
- She attended the Barnard College in New York, where she studied French and economics. She also received her master's degree in creative writing from Brown University, Rhode Island.
- She is a strong advocate for the rights of Haitians living in the United States.
- She has collaborated on documentaries about the violence and civil rights movement in Haiti.

The story you'll be reading is an excerpt from her 2004 novel The Dew Breaker. The story is about a riot in politically unstable Haiti, as seen through the eyes of a young boy.

Awards include:
- Pushcart Short Story Prize (1995)
- American Book Award (1999)
- Finalist: National Book Critic's Circle Award for Fiction
- Finalist: Pen/Faulkner Award
- Washington Post Book World Notable Book

Works include:
- *Breath, Eyes, Memory*
- *Krik? Krak!*
- *The Farming of Bones*
- *Behind the Mountains*
- *The Dew Breaker*
- *The Beacon Best of 2000*
- *The Butterfly's Way*
- *After the Dance*
- *Courage and Pain*
- *The Agronomist*

Story Set-Up ...

In Chapter 4, you explored stories about people's experiences and learned how writers are able to hook readers into their stories. In this story, we read the account of a young boy who lives through the difficulties of his country's political instability. How does a twelve-year-old boy experience the riots in his hometown? What will happen to him and his family? Is his best friend safe from the demonstrators?

Now ... to the Story!

Before Reading

ACTIVITY 1

» Using the suffixes "hood" or "ship," change the following words in the grid below to abstract nouns.

» What do the new words mean? How are they reflected in the story?

mother	hard	dictator	boy	friend
adult	neighbor	relation	leader	man

ACTIVITY 2

» Look up the words "dew breaker" separately. Keeping in mind that the Haitian people experienced many atrocities during the Duvalier regime, what do you think this Creole expression means?

During Reading

» As you read, remember to notice the sensory details the author uses to draw you into the story.

» Which senses do the following quotes appeal to?

Quotes:

"She was winded from all the excitement outside, forcing air out of her lungs while trying to contain a sudden bout of hiccups." (line 3)

"Keeping her eyes closed, she felt for the rosary around her neck, and between hiccups and deep breaths whispered, "Jesus, Mary, Saint Joseph, please watch over Michel and me."" (line 5)

"The sound of a large crowd stomping through the alley between Monsieur Christophe's water station and our house seemed to be what was making the cot rattle ..." (line 9)

"... she raised a corner of her skirt and used it to wipe the sweat from her forehead" (line 59)

"... slipped me some of his mother's money now and then for candy and ice cream" (line 109)

❯ As you read, fill in a sensory chart with nouns and verbs from the story that help you really experience the text.

Sensory chart:

Sight	Sound	Taste	Touch
Examples ...	Examples ...	Examples ...	Examples ...

THE DEW BREAKER

By Edwidge Danticat

Mother and I cowered beneath her *cot* after a small rock pierced the sheet of plastic she'd draped over our bedroom window the week before as extra protection against the alley *mosquitoes*. She was *winded* from all the excitement outside, forcing air out of her lungs
005> while trying to contain a sudden bout of *hiccups*. Keeping her eyes closed, she felt for the *rosary* around her neck, and between hiccups and deep breaths whispered, "Jesus, Mary, Saint Joseph, please watch over Michel and me."

The sound of a large *crowd* stomping through the alley between
010> Monsieur Christophe's water station and our house seemed to be what was making the cot *rattle*, rather than Mother's and my shaking bodies. Above the echoes of drums, horns, bamboo flutes, and conch shells, we heard voices shouting, "Come out, *macoutes*! Come out, macoutes!" daring members of the Volunteers for National Security
015> *militia* to appear from wherever they were hiding.

Overnight our country had completely changed. We had fallen asleep under a *dictatorship* headed by a *pudgy* thirty-four-year-old man and his glamorous wife. During the night they'd *sneaked away*—I had to see the television images myself before I could believe it—the wife
020> *ornately* made up, her long brown hair hidden under a white *turban*, her carefully manicured fingers holding a long cigarette, the husband at the wheel of the family's BMW, driving his wife and himself to the *tarmac* of an airport named after his dead father, from whom he'd inherited the country at nineteen, to an American airplane that would
025> carry them to permanent *exile* in France. The presidential couple's *reign* had ended, his having lasted fifteen years and hers the span of their six-year marriage. Their departure, however, orphaned a large number of loyal militiamen, who had guarded the couple's command with all types of vicious acts. Now the population was going after those

030> militiamen, those macoutes, with the determination of an army in the middle of its biggest battle to date.

My cousin Vaval, who'd left the house at ***dawn*** to catch a camion to the provinces, but then had ***postponed*** his trip to come back and ***brief*** us on what was going on, told us how, on his way to the bus depot, he had
035> seen a group of people tie one of these militiamen to a lamppost, pour gasoline down his throat, and set him on fire. The ***flock*** making its way through the alley behind our house was probably on a similar quest for vengeance, most likely looking for a man called Regulus, who lived nearby. Regulus's eighteen-year-old son, Romain, was my hero and the
040> person whom at that time I considered my best friend.

It didn't take long for the crowd to move past our house. I had to remind myself that these men and women, old and young, meant no ***harm*** to people like us, people like Mother, Vaval, and me. Vaval was so certain of this that he was standing out in front of the house watching the
045> crowd, as though it was an ordinary parade going by. Mother, however,

Glossary

cot: small bed that folds up
mosquitoes: small insects that suck blood
winded: out of breath
hiccups: involuntary sounds from the mouth
rosary: sting of beads used for praying
crowd: large group of people
rattle: move with a sharp sound
macoutes: secret police who tortured and killed civilians; torturers
militia: military
dictatorship: government possessing absolute power

pudgy: plump; a bit fat
sneaked away: left without being noticed
ornately: elaborately
turban: headdress
tarmac: ground where airplane waits
exile: expulsion from home country
reign: royal rule or authority
dawn: first daylight in the morning
postponed: changed to a later time
brief: give a summary
flock: large number of people
harm: physical injury

whose **creed** in life was something like "It's harder for trouble to find you under your bed" (yes, I know there are many ways she could have been proven wrong), had thought that it would be best for us to hide. The rock coming through the window reinforced her case. I couldn't
050> help but be **frightened**. I was twelve-years-old, and, according to my mother, three months before my birth I had lost my father to something my mother would only vaguely describe as "political," making me part of a generation of mostly fatherless boys, though some of our fathers were still living, even if somewhere else—in the
055> provinces, in another country, or across the alley not **acknowledging us**. A great many of our fathers had also died in the dictatorship's prisons, and others had abandoned us altogether to serve the regime.

My mother's hiccups **subsided**. Judging that the crowd had moved a safe enough distance from our house, she raised a corner of her skirt
060> and used it to **wipe** the sweat from her forehead, crossed herself several times, then **crawled out** from under the cot. She waited for me to come out, then sat on the cot's edge and dusted a film of white **grime** from her knees.

"I knew that girl was not *sweeping* all the way under the beds," my
065> mother said, quickly reverting to her normal *griping* self, perhaps to
erase the image in my mind of her *cowering* with fear under the cot.
The "girl" she was referring to was Rosie, a distant cousin my mother
had *summoned* from the provinces to do such things as cook and
wash and sweep under beds, when she'd promised Rosie's poor peasant
070> parents that she'd be sending her to school. In fact, the only education
Rosie was getting was from talking to the people who came to buy colas
at a busy intersection, where my mother stationed her when Rosie
wasn't inside the house cooking, washing, and not sweeping under the
beds. Being madly in love with Rosie—Rosie's bloodline was separate
075> enough from mine that I could have married her had I been older—
I didn't blame her at all for the *dust balls* under the cot, but I knew
better than to defend her to my mother, who would have turned her
anger at Rosie on me.

All the commotion with the departure of our *despised* leader and his
080> wife and the crowd passing through the neighbourhood had made
me hungry. But what I wanted most to do was *head over* to Romain's
house and make sure he was okay. Like us, Romain and his mother
had nothing to fear from our angry neighbors. It was Romain's father,

Glossary

creed: belief
frightened: scared
acknowledging us:
admitting that we exist
subsided: lessened
wipe: clean
crawled out: moved on hands
and knees
grime: dirt
sweeping: cleaning the floor
with a broom

griping: complaining
cowering: staying down because
of fear
summoned: called for a specific
purpose
dust balls: balls of dust (for example,
that accumulate under a bed)
despised: hated
head over: go to

Regulus, they wanted. He'd **beaten** them **up** and stolen money and
085> property from most of them and had put many of their relatives
in jail or in the **grave**. In addition to his other crimes, Regulus had
abandoned Romain when Romain was a month old. Romain had
never called his father Papa but, like everyone else, referred to him
as Regulus, his last name, which Romain didn't even have.

090> Romain and I had met when I was about eight-years-old. His mother
and mine had become friends, taking turns visiting each other every
evening to catch up at the end of the day. I would accompany my
mother on her visits to his house, and while our mothers sat inside and
chatted, we would play marbles or kick a soccer ball around out front.

095> Unlike many of the older boys, Romain didn't have many friends and
didn't seem to **resent** having to play with a **runt** like me. In fact, he
even appeared to like it and came around to my house most Sunday
afternoons to ask my mother if he could take me to a kung fu movie
or for a bike ride on Champs de Mars plaza.

100> Our mothers had a **falling-out** one day—neither Romain nor I was
ever able to find out from either of them what it was about—and
I stopped visiting Romain's house with my mother and he stopped
coming around to ask my mother's permission to take me places.
Our **outings** became less frequent, but every once in a while we'd
105> plot to meet somewhere and then proceed to a karate **flick**, especially
if it was a new Bruce Lee.

Romain knew what it was like to be an only child. And maybe this
is why he always watched out for me, stepped in if I was in a **scuffle**
with some other kid from the neighborhood, slipped me some of his
110> mother's money now and then for candy and ice cream, and invited
me over to his house whenever his mother was away. His maid,
Auberte, would prepare whatever I wanted to eat, whether it was
good for me or not. While we ate Auberte's delicious fried sweets,
I would listen to Romain talk and talk, mostly quoting lines from

115> books I'd never read and writers I'd never heard of. Even though I rarely understood everything he said, I was grateful that he was speaking to me, like a peer, like a man.

Looking back now, I realize how much I needed someone like Romain in my life. He must have felt this too. Come to think of it, aside from
120> Rosie and Vaval, who were always too busy with my mother's chores to spend much time with me, Romain was my only friend.

Glossary

beaten up: hurt physically
grave: place in the ground to bury the dead
resent: feel unhappy after an injury or insult
runt: a small person or animal
falling-out: disagreement
outings: excursions
flick: movie
scuffle: fight

Exploring the Story ...

𝒞 After Reading

ACTIVITY 1

❯❯ Sometimes stories have many characters. Of course, the main characters play an essential role in what happens. But secondary characters, who might not seem significant at first, often play a vital role as well. Briefly explain the role of the various characters in the story *The Dew Breaker*.

Character chart:

Main characters	Secondary characters
Role in the story ...	Role in the story ...

ACTIVITY 2

❯❯ Reread the story to the end of line 15.

a) Where are the narrator and his mother at the beginning of the story?

b) How do we know that the narrator's mother is a religious woman?

c) What is the narrator's name?

d) Who are the "macoutes"?

❯❯ Now reread from lines 16–40.

e) Why do you think the dictator left?

f) Why does the narrator say that the dictator's departure "orphaned a large number of loyal militiamen"?

g) Why were the people looking for the macoutes?

h) In your own words, explain why Vaval returned to the city.

i) Why do you think the narrator thought of Romain as a hero?

❯ Continue rereading from lines 41–63.

j) Why does the narrator say that the rioters meant no harm to "people like us"?

k) How do we know that Vaval was not afraid?

l) Why did the mother decide to hide under the bed?

m) What happened to many of the young boys' fathers?

n) What do you think happened to the narrator's father?

o) What indications do we have that the mother was scared?

❯ Next reread from line 64–78.

p) Who is Rosie and where is she from?

q) What is Rosie supposed to be doing in the city? What is she doing instead?

r) What do you think of the narrator's mother?

❯ Finally, reread from line 79 to the end of the story.

s) What relationship did Romain have with his father?

t) Why do you think Romain didn't have many friends?

u) Why did Romain protect the narrator?

v) How do we know that Romain's family and the narrator's family are well-off financially?

ACTIVITY 3

» Establishing the relationships that exist between the different characters is an important part of storytelling. Describe the relationship the <u>narrator</u> has with the characters below. Use quotes and examples from the story to explain your point of view.

• his mother

• Rosie

• Vaval

• Romain

• his father

D Your Thoughts?

i. How do you think the narrator feels about the riots? What are his feelings about the fleeing dictator? Support your opinions with examples from the story.

ii. Why do you think the story is titled *The Dew Breaker*? Who is the author referring to?

iii. What do you think happens to Romain?

E Links to Chapter 4 ...

i. What are some of the similarities between this story and "A Long Way Gone"? (Ch. 4)

ii. Find the scene in *The Dew Breaker* that hooks your attention the most. Explain why.

iii. What parts of this story do you think are true and what parts do you think are based on fact?

Is He Living or Is He Dead?

Mark Twain

Have you ever heard of Tom Sawyer or Huckleberry Finn? They are two of the many unforgettable characters that were created by the great American writer Mark Twain. Twain's real name was Samuel Langhorne Clemens. His writing is loved for its honesty, humour and wit.

Born: November 30, 1835, in Florida, Missouri

Quote: "Twenty years from now, you will be more disappointed by the things that you didn't do than by the ones you did do. … Explore. Dream. Discover."

More about Mark Twain

- In 1847, when he was 12, his father died. Soon after, he left school to work as a printer's apprentice.
- In 1858, Samuel Clemens became a riverboat pilot and spent years piloting up and down the Mississippi. This experience enriched his writing.
- Even though Mark Twain was a popular writer, he made bad financial decisions and had to give lectures to earn enough money to get out of debt.
- Many of his novels, like *The Adventures of Huckleberry Finn*, are American literary classics.

The short story that you'll be reading, "Is He Living or Is He Dead?," was written in 1893.

Awards include:
- honorary degrees from both Yale and Oxford universities;
- being admitted to the American Academy of Arts and Letters in 1904.

Works include:
- *The Celebrated Jumping Frog of Calaveras County*
- *Roughing It*
- *The Prince and the Pauper*
- *A Connecticut Yankee in King Arthur's Court*
- *Life on the Mississippi*
- *The Adventures of Tom Sawyer*
- *The Adventures of Huckleberry Finn*
- *A Tramp Abroad*
- *Is He Dead?*
- *A Curious Dream and other Sketches*
- *Merry Tales*
- *A Dog's Tale*
- *A Horse's Tale*
- *The Diaries of Adam and Eve*
- *Colonel Sellers*
- *The Innocents Abroad*

Story Set-Up ...

In Chapter 5, you looked at the advantages and disadvantages of leaving your comfort zone. You discussed difficulties you might have to endure on the road to success. In the following story, you will read about the problems some painters encounter as they attempt to achieve greatness. What price will they have to pay in order to prosper?

Now ... to the Story!

𝒜 Before Reading

ACTIVITY 1

❯ Associate the following words from the story with an appropriate meaning:

a) wandered (v.)		i.	supplies; collections
b) starving (v.)		ii.	initials
c) stock (n.)		iii.	journalists
d) cast lots (v.)		iv.	walked in no specific direction
e) cipher (n.)		v.	mannequin doll
f) dummy (n.)		vi.	choose objects as a way to decide something
g) correspondents (n.)			
h) waste away (v.)		vii.	being extremely hungry
		viii.	deteriorate in health

ACTIVITY 2

❯ Read the following statements and decide where you stand on a scale of 1 (completely agree) to 5 (completely disagree). Be ready to defend your point of view with your classmates.

Statements:

- You have to feel a lot of discomfort before you decide to change your life.

- All famous painters were poor during their lifetime.

- In order to be truly well-known, you have to be dead.

- People will believe anything you tell them.

- Art is about marketing, not about talent.

ACTIVITY 3

> Read the title of the story and skim through the pages. Who do you think the story will be about?

ℬ During Reading

> Look at the descriptive language the author uses. Write down some phrases that you think are particularly effective:

Example:

Descriptive language	... the balmy air and the brilliant blue sea

> Look for examples of the following themes in the story:

- friendship
- pride
- mortality
- poverty

IS HE LIVING OR IS HE DEAD?

By Mark Twain

I was spending the month of March 1892 at Mentone, in the Riviera. At this retired spot one has all the advantages, privately, which are to be had publicly at Monte Carlo and Nice, a few miles farther along. That is to say, one has the flooding sunshine, the **balmy** air and the
005> brilliant blue sea, without the **marring** additions of human pow-wow and fuss and feathers and display. Mentone is quiet, simple, restful, unpretentious; the rich and the **gaudy** do not come there. As a rule, I mean, the rich do not come there. Now and then a rich man comes, and I presently got acquainted with one of these. Partially to disguise
010> him I will call him Smith. One day, in the Hotel des Anglais, at the second breakfast, he exclaimed:

"Quick! Cast your eye on the man going out at the door. Take in every detail of him."

"Why?"

015> "Do you know who he is?"

"Yes. He spent several days here before you came. He is an old, retired, and very rich silk manufacturer from Lyons, they say, and I guess he is alone in the world, for he always looks sad and dreamy, and doesn't talk with anybody. His name is Theophile Magnan."

020> I supposed that Smith would now proceed to justify the large interest which he had shown in Monsieur Magnan, but, instead, he dropped into a **brown study**, and was apparently lost to me and to the rest of the world during some minutes. Now and then he passed his fingers through his flossy white hair, to assist his thinking, and meantime
025> he allowed his breakfast to go on cooling. At last he said:

"No, it's gone; I can't call it back."

"Can't call what back?"

"It's one of Hans Andersen's beautiful little stories. But it's gone
from me. Part of it is like this: A child has a caged bird, which it loves,
030> but thoughtlessly neglects. The bird *pours out* its song unheard and
unheeded; but, in time, hunger and thirst *assail* the creature, and its
song grows plaintive and feeble and finally ceases—the bird dies. The
child comes, and is *smitten* to the heart with remorse: then, with bitter
tears and lamentations, it calls its mates, and they bury the bird with
035> elaborate pomp and the tenderest grief, without knowing, poor things,
that it isn't children only who starve poets to death and then spend
enough on their funerals and monuments to have kept them alive
and made them easy and comfortable. Now—"

But here we were interrupted. About ten that evening I ran across
040> Smith, and he asked me up to his parlour to help him smoke and
drink hot Scotch. It was a cosy place, with its comfortable chairs,
its cheerful lamps, and its friendly open fire of seasoned olive-wood.
To make everything perfect, there was a *muffled* booming of the surf
outside. After the second Scotch and much lazy and contented chat,
045> Smith said:

"Now we are properly primed—I to tell a curious history and you
to listen to it. It has been a secret for many years—a secret between
me and three others; but I am going to
break the seal now. Are you comfortable?"

050> "Perfectly. Go on."

Here follows what he told me:

"A long time ago I was a young
artist—a very young artist,
in fact—and I wandered about
055> the country parts of France,
sketching here and sketching there,
and was presently joined by a couple
of darling young Frenchmen who were

Glossary

balmy: mild; temperate
marring: damaging
gaudy: flashy
brown study: deep thought
pours out: spills out;
discharges
unheeded: ignored
assail: attack
smitten: obsessed
muffled: muted

at the same kind of thing that I was doing. We were as happy as we
060> were poor, or as poor as we were happy—phrase it to suit yourself.
Claude Frere and Carl Boulanger—these are the names of those boys;
dear, dear fellows, and the sunniest spirits that ever laughed at poverty
and had a noble good time in all weathers.

"At last we ran hard aground in a Breton village, and an artist as poor as
065> ourselves took us in and literally saved us from starving—Francois Millet."

"What! The great Francois Millet?"

"Great? He wasn't any greater than we were, then. He hadn't any fame,
even in his own village; and he was so poor that he hadn't anything
to feed us on but *turnips*, and even the turnips failed us sometimes.
070> We four became fast friends, *doting* friends, inseparables. We painted
away together with all our might, piling up stock, piling up stock, but
very *seldom* getting rid of any of it. We had lovely times together;
but, O my soul! How we were *pinched* now and then!

"For a little over two years this went on. At last, one day, Claude said:

075> "'Boys, we've come to the end. Do you understand that?—absolutely
to the end. Everybody has struck—there's a league formed against us.
I've been all around the village and it's just as I tell you. They refuse to
credit us for another centime until all the odds and ends are paid up.'

"This struck us as cold. Every face was blank with *dismay*. We realised
080> that our circumstances were desperate now. There was a long silence.
Finally, Millet said with a sigh:

"'Nothing occurs to me—nothing. Suggest something, lads.'

"There was no response, unless a *mournful* silence may be called
a response. Carl got up, and walked nervously up and down a while,
085> then said:

"'It's a shame! Look at these canvases: stacks and stacks of as good
pictures as anybody in Europe paints—I don't care who he is. Yes, and
plenty of *lounging* strangers have said the same—or nearly that, anyway.'

"'But didn't buy,' Millet said.

090> "'No matter, they said it; and it's true, too. Look at your "Angelus" there! Will anybody tell me—'

"'Pah, Carl—My "Angelus!" I was offered five francs for it.'

"'When?'

"'Who offered it?'

095> "'Where is he?'

"'Why didn't you take it?'

"'Come—don't all speak at once. I thought he would give more—I was sure of it—he looked it—so I asked him eight.'

"'Well—and then?'

100> "'He said he would call again.'

"'Thunder and lightning! Why, Francois—'

"'Oh, I know—I know! It was a mistake, and I was a fool. Boys, I meant for the best; you'll grant me that, and I—'

"'Why, certainly, we know that, bless your dear heart; but don't you
105> be a fool again.'

"'I? I wish somebody would come along and offer us a *cabbage* for it—you'd see!'

"'A cabbage! Oh, don't name it—it makes my mouth water. Talk
110> of things less *trying*.'

"'Boys,' said Carl, 'do these pictures lack merit? Answer me that.'

"'No!'

Glossary

turnips: yellow root vegetables
doting: devoted
seldom: rarely
pinched: short of money
dismay: apprehension
mournful: sad
lounging: lazy; idle
cabbage: leafy vegetable
trying: frustrating

"'Aren't they of very great and high merit? Answer me that.'

115> "'Yes.'

"'Of such great and high merit that, if an illustrious name were attached to them they would sell at splendid prices. Isn't it so?'

"'Certainly it is. Nobody doubts that.'

"'But—I'm not joking—isn't it so?'

120> "'Why, of course it's so—and we are not joking. But what of it. What of it? How does that concern us '

"'In this way, comrades—we'll attach an illustrious name to them!'

"The lively conversation stopped. The faces were turned inquiringly upon Carl. What sort of *riddle* might this be? Where was an illustrious
125> name to be *borrowed*? And who was to borrow it?

"Carl sat down, and said:

"'Now, I have a perfectly serious thing to propose. I think it is the only way to keep us out of the *almshouse*, and I believe it to be a perfectly sure way. I base this opinion upon certain multitudinous and long-
130> established facts in human history. I believe my project will make us all rich.'

"'Rich! You've lost your mind.'

"'No, I haven't.'

"'Yes, you have—you've lost your mind. What do you call rich?'

135> "'A hundred thousand francs apiece.'

"'He has lost his mind. I knew it.'

"'Yes, he has. Carl, privation has been too much for you, and—'

"'Carl, you want to take a pill and get right to bed.'

"'Bandage him first—bandage his head, and then—'

140> "'No, bandage his heels; his brains have been settling for weeks—
I've noticed it.'

"'Shut up!' said Millet, with ostensible severity, 'and let the boy have
his say. Now, then—come out with your project, Carl. What is it?'

"'Well, then, by way of preamble I will ask you to note this fact in
145> human history: that the merit of many a great artist has never been
acknowledged until after he was starved and dead. This has happened
so often that I make bold to *found* a law upon it. This law: that the
merit of every great unknown and neglected artist must and will
be recognised and his pictures climb to high prices after his death.
150> My project is this: we must cast lots—one of us must die.'

"The remark fell so calmly and so unexpectedly that we almost forgot
to jump. Then there was a wild chorus of advice again—medical
advice—for the help of Carl's brain; but he waited patiently for the
hilarity to calm down, and then went on again with his project:

155> "'Yes, one of us must die, to save the others—and himself. We will
cast lots. The one chosen shall be illustrious, all of us shall be rich.
Hold still, now—hold still; don't interrupt—I tell you I know what
I am talking about. Here is the idea. During the next three months
the one who is to die shall paint with all his might, enlarge his stock all
160> he can—not pictures, no! Skeleton sketches, studies, parts of studies,
fragments of studies, a dozen dabs of the brush on each—meaningless,
of course, but his, with his cipher on them; turn out fifty a day, each
to contain some peculiarity or
mannerism easily detectable as
165> his—they're the things that sell, you
know, and are collected at fabulous
prices for the world's museums, after
the great man is gone; we'll have a ton
of them ready—a ton! And all that time
170> the rest of us will be busy supporting
the *moribund*, and working Paris

Glossary

riddle: puzzle
borrowed: took something
and promise to return it
almshouse: poorhouse
found: establish
moribund: a person
who is dying

and the dealers—preparations for the coming event, you know; and when everything is hot and just right, we'll spring the death on them and have the notorious funeral. You get the idea?'

175> "'N-o; at least, not qu—'

"'Not quite? Don't you see? The man doesn't really die; he changes his name and vanishes; we bury a dummy, and cry over it, with all the world to help. And I—'

"But he wasn't allowed to finish. Everybody broke out into a ***rousing***
180> hurrah of applause; and all jumped up and ***capered*** about the room and fell on each other's necks in transports of gratitude and joy. For hours we talked over the great plan, without ever feeling hungry; and at last, when all the details had been arranged satisfactorily, we cast lots and Millet was elected—elected to die, as we called it. Then we scraped
185> together those things which one never parts with until he is betting them against future wealth—***keepsake trinkets*** and suchlike—and these we ***pawned*** for enough to furnish us a frugal farewell supper and breakfast, and leave us a few francs over for travel, and a ***stake*** of turnips and such for Millet to live on for a few days.

190> "Next morning, early, the three of us cleared out, straightway after breakfast—on foot, of course. Each of us carried a dozen of Millet's small pictures, purposing to market them. Carl struck for Paris, where he would start the work of building up Millet's name against the coming great day. Claude and I were to separate, and ***scatter***
195> abroad over France.

"Now, it will surprise you to know what an easy and comfortable thing we had. I walked two days before I began business. Then I began to sketch a villa in the outskirts of a big town—because I saw the proprietor standing on an upper veranda. He came down to look
200> on—I thought he would. I worked swiftly, intending to keep him interested. Occasionally he fired off a little ejaculation of approbation, and by-and-by he spoke up with enthusiasm, and said I was a master!

"I put down my brush, reached into my satchel, fetched out a Millet, and
205> pointed to the cipher in the corner. I said, proudly:

"'I suppose you recognise that? Well, he taught me! I should think I ought to know my trade!'

210> "The man looked guiltily embarrassed, and was silent. I said sorrowfully:

"'You don't mean to intimate that you don't know the cipher of Francois Millet!'

"Of course he didn't know that cipher; but he was the gratefullest man
215> you ever saw, just the same, for being let out of an uncomfortable place on such easy terms. He said:

"'No! Why, it is Millet's, sure enough! I don't know what I could have been thinking of. Of course I recognise it now.'

"Next, he wanted to buy it; but I said that, although I wasn't rich, I wasn't
220> that poor. However, at last, I let him have it for eight hundred francs."

"Eight hundred!"

"Yes. Millet would have sold it for a pork chop. Yes, I got eight hundred
225> francs for that little thing. I wish I could get it back for eighty thousand. But that time's gone by. I made a very nice picture of that man's house and I wanted to offer it to him for ten francs, but that
230> wouldn't answer, seeing I was the pupil

Glossary

rousing: inspiring; energetic
capered: jumped around
keepsake: memento; souvenir
trinkets: little ornaments
pawned: exchanged for money
stake: share
scatter: disperse

of such a master, so I sold it to him for a hundred. I sent the eight hundred francs straight to Millet from that town and **struck out** again next day.

"But I didn't walk—no. I rode. I have ridden ever since. I sold
235> one picture every day, and never tried to sell two. I always said to my customer:

"'I am a fool to sell a picture of Francois Millet's at all, for that man is not going to live three months, and when he dies, his pictures can't be had for love or money.'

240> "I took care to spread that little fact as far as I could, and prepare the world for the event.

"I take credit to myself for our plan of selling the pictures—it was mine. I suggested it that last evening when we were laying out our campaign, and all three of us agreed to give it a good fair trial before
245> giving it up for some other. It succeeded with all of us. I walked only two days, Claude walked two—both of us afraid to make Millet celebrated too close to home—but Carl walked only half a day, the bright, conscienceless rascal, and after that he travelled like a duke.

"Every now and then we got in with a country editor and started an
250> item around through the press; not an item announcing that a new painter had been discovered, but an item which **let on** that everybody knew Francois Millet; not an item praising him in any way, but merely a word concerning the present condition of the "master"—sometimes

hopeful, sometimes despondent, but always ***tinged*** with fears for the
255> worst. We always marked these paragraphs, and sent the papers to all
the people who had bought pictures of us.

"Carl was soon in Paris and he worked things with a high hand.
He made friends with the correspondents, and got Millet's condition
reported to England and all over the continent, and America,
260> and everywhere.

"At the end of six weeks from the start, we three met in Paris and called
a halt, and stopped sending back to Millet for additional pictures. The
boom was so high, and everything so ripe, that we saw that it would be
a mistake not to strike now, right away, without waiting any longer. So
265> we wrote Millet to go to bed and begin to waste away pretty fast, for we
should like him to die in ten days if he could get ready.

"Then we figured up and found that among us we had sold eighty-five
small pictures and studies, and had sixty-nine thousand francs to show
for it. Carl had made the last sale and the most brilliant one of all. He sold
270> the 'Angelus' for twenty-two hundred francs. How we did glorify
him!—not foreseeing that a day was coming by-and-by when France
would struggle to own it and a stranger would capture it for five hundred
and fifty thousand, cash.

"We had a wind-up champagne supper that night, and next day Claude
275> and I packed up and went off to nurse Millet through his last days and
keep ***busybodies*** out of the house and
send daily bulletins to Carl in Paris
for publication in the papers of several
continents for the information of
280> a waiting world. The sad end came
at last, and Carl was there in time
to help in the final mournful ***rites***.

"You remember that great funeral, and
what a stir it made all over the globe,
285> and how the illustrious of two worlds

Glossary

struck out: set out; started
let on: pretended; made
believe
tinged: touched
busybodies: people who
interfere in other people's
business
rites: burial

came to attend it and testify their sorrow. We four—still inseparable—carried the coffin, and would allow none to help. And we were right about that, because it hadn't anything in it but a wax figure, and any other coffin-bearers would have ***found fault*** with the weight. Yes, we
290> same old four, who had lovingly shared privation together in the old hard times now gone forever, carried the cof—"

"Which four?"

"We four—for Millet helped to carry his own coffin. In disguise, you know. Disguised as a relative—distant relative."

295> "Astonishing!"

"But true just the same. Well, you remember how the pictures went up. Money? We didn't know what to do with it. There's a man in Paris today who owns seventy Millet pictures. He paid us two million francs for them. And as for the ***bushels*** of sketches and studies which Millet
300> shovelled out during the six weeks that we were on the road, well, it would astonish you to know the figure we sell them at nowadays—that is, when we consent to let one go!"

"It is a wonderful history, perfectly wonderful!"

"Yes—it amounts to that."

305> "Whatever became of Millet?"

"Can you keep a secret?"

"I can."

"Do you remember the man I called your attention to in the dining room today? That was Francois Millet."

310> "Great—"

> ### Glossary
> **found fault:** protested; criticized
> **bushels:** large amounts

"Scott! Yes. For once they didn't starve a genius to death and then put into other pockets the rewards he should have had himself. This songbird was not allowed to pipe out its heart unheard and then be paid with the cold pomp of a big funeral. We looked out for that."

Exploring the Story ...

C After Reading

ACTIVITY 1

» Mark Twain often writes a "story within a story." Create
a version of the chart below to help you distinguish between
the two stories in "Is He Living or Is He Dead?" Compare
the stories orally or in writing.

Plot sequence chart:

Story 1	Story 2
Setting	Setting
Characters	Characters
Conflict	Conflict
Climax	Climax
Resolution	Resolution

ACTIVITY 2

» Reread the story to the end of line 49.

a) In your own words, explain the fable of the caged bird
by Hans Andersen.

b) Why do you think Smith tells the narrator the fable
of the caged bird?

» Now reread from lines 50–110.

c) Why do you think the narrator was surprised when Mr. Smith
said he had stayed with Francois Millet?

d) Why did the villagers refuse to give the young painters credit?

e) Why did Millet refuse five francs for his painting called "Angelus"?

◆ **Continue rereading from lines 111–175.**

f) In your own words, explain the "law" that Carl talks about.

g) How do the other painters react to Carl's solution?

◆ **Now reread lines 176–248.**

h) How does Carl's "law" become a solution for the painters?

i) Who is elected to "die"?

j) In his conversation with the proprietor of the villa, how does the narrator imply that Millet is famous?

k) Why is it ironic that the narrator sold the proprietor of the villa a painting by Millet for eight hundred francs?

l) After reading this section, what do you think is Twain's opinion of people who buy art?

◆ **Then reread lines 249–304.**

m) Why do you think that Carl was now able to sell Millet's Angelus for twenty-two hundred francs when, before, Millet could not get eight francs for it?

n) What happened to Millet?

◆ **Finally, reread from line 305 to the end of the story.**

o) Who was Francois Millet?

p) Why does the narrator refer to the fable of the caged bird at the end of his narration?

𝒟 Your Thoughts?

i. What do you think is the moral of the story?

ii. What do you think Francois Millet's obituary would have been like? Write what you think it might have said.

iii. Trust is an important theme in Twain's stories. How is it portrayed here?

iv. Would you sacrifice your identity in order to become famous? Explain.

𝓔 Links to Chapter 5 ...

i. Do you think the painters were right to leave the village and try to find success while they wandered through France? Explain.

ii. In the story, the young artists come up with an ingenious plan because they are in trouble. Do you agree that people come up with better solutions when they feel a certain amount of discomfort? Explain.

iii. Do you think that Francois Millet found a new comfort zone when he adopted his new identity? Why or why not?

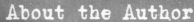

Kate Chopin

The American writer Kate Chopin was far ahead of her time. She wrote about issues that were not normally discussed in "polite society." These issues usually dealt with the unfair restrictions that she and the women around her endured. This earned her praise from some quarters, but lots of criticism too.

Born: July 12, 1850, in St. Louis, Missouri

Quote: "… to succeed, the artist must possess the courageous soul … the brave soul. The soul that dares and defies."

More about Kate Chopin

- Kate Chopin was born Catherine (Kate) O'Flaherty in St. Louis, Missouri in 1850 to Eliza and Thomas O'Flaherty. She was the third of five children and the only child to live past the age of twenty-five.
- In 1855, at age five and a half, she was sent to the St. Louis Academy of the Sacred Heart, a Catholic boarding school. She won medals and delivered the commencement address.
- In 1870, at the age of twenty, she married Oscar Chopin, twenty-five, the son of a wealthy cotton-growing family in Louisiana. He was from a French Catholic background, as was Kate. After their marriage, they lived in New Orleans, where she had five boys and two girls before she was twenty-eight.
- Oscar died of malaria there in 1882; then Kate ran his general store and plantation for over a year.

More about Kate Chopin (continued)

- To support herself and her young family, she began to write. She wrote two novels and about a hundred short stories in the 1890s. Her second novel, *The Awakening*, published in 1899, was criticized at the time for being "vulgar," but is now recognized as a fine portrait of the society she knew so well.

Awards include:

- honorary degrees from both Yale and Oxford universities;
- being admitted to the American Academy of Arts and Letters in 1904.

Works include:

- *At Fault*
- *The Awakening*
- *A Night in Acadia*
- *Mrs. Mobrey's Reason*
- *A Shameful Affair*
- *A Respectable Woman*
- *The Wood Choppers*
- *Polly*

Story Set-Up ...

In Chopin's world (late 1800s), marriage was the principal goal of every woman's life. And once a woman was married, her job was to care for her husband and children. Any other wishes or objectives she might have were not considered important. Kate Chopin rejected this idea and, in her writing, she dared to address matters that, till then, were kept completely private: happiness with one's life, sexuality, the desire to be in control, etc.

The story you are about to read deals with one woman's reaction to her husband's death. Is she devastated? Is she relieved? Is she drowning in sorrow, or is she full of hope for the future? Read the story and find out. Then answer the questions that follow.

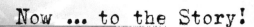
$\mathscr{A}$ Before Reading

ACTIVITY 1

» Match the following words from the story with an appropriate meaning:

a) hastened (v.)		i.	quick
b) wept (v.)		ii.	disturbed
c) sudden (adj.)		iii.	in confusion
d) haunted (v.)		iv.	desire
e) gaze (n.)		v.	request
f) tumultuously (adv.)		vi.	moved quickly
g) bitter (adj.)		vii.	spirit
h) will (n.)		viii.	look
i) soul (n.)		ix.	unpleasant
j) prayer (n.)		x.	cried

ACTIVITY 2

» Keeping in mind the era in which Chopin wrote "The Story of an Hour" and the issues that she often wrote about, read the following paragraph and predict what you think the story might be about.

"Knowing that Mrs. Mallard was afflicted with heart trouble, great care was taken to break to her as gently as possible the news of her husband's death."

ℬ During Reading

❯ Look at the descriptive language the author uses. Write down some phrases that you think are particularly effective:

Example:

Descriptive language
delicious breath of rain
trees were all aquiver

THE STORY OF AN HOUR

By Kate Chopin

Knowing that Mrs. Mallard was **_afflicted_** with heart trouble, great care was taken to break to her as gently as possible the news of her husband's death.

It was her sister Josephine who told her, in broken sentences; her
005> husband's friend Richards was there, too, near her. It was he who had been in the newspaper office when news of the railroad disaster was received, with Brently Mallard's name leading the list of "killed." He had taken the time to assure himself of its truth by a second telegram and had hastened to **_forestall_** any less careful, less tender friend in
010> **_bearing_** the sad message.

She did not hear the story as many women have heard the same, with a paralyzed inability to accept its significance. She wept at once,

with sudden, wild abandonment, in her sister's arms. When the storm of grief had ***spent*** itself, she went away to her room alone. She would
015> have no one follow her.

A comfortable roomy armchair stood there, facing the open window. She sank into this, pressed down by a physical exhaustion that haunted her body and seemed to reach into her soul.

She could see in the open square before her house the tops of trees
020> that were all ***aquiver*** with the new spring life. The delicious breath of rain was in the air. In the street below, a ***peddler*** was ***crying his wares***. The notes of a distant song, which someone was singing, reached her faintly, and countless sparrows were singing in the eaves.

There were patches of blue sky showing here and there through the
025> clouds that had met and piled one above the other in the west facing her window.

She sat with her head thrown back upon the cushion of the chair, quite motionless, except when a sob came up into her
030> throat and shook her, as a child who has cried itself to sleep continues to sob in its dreams.

She was young, with a fair, calm face, whose lines ***bespoke*** repression and
035> even a certain strength. But now there was a dull ***stare*** in her eyes, whose gaze was fixed away ***off yonder*** on one of those patches of blue sky. It was not a glance of reflection,
040> but rather indicated a suspension of intelligent thought.

There was something coming to her and she was waiting for it, fearfully.

Glossary

afflicted: was sick with something
forestall: act in advance in order to prevent something from happening
bearing: bringing
spent: consumed; used up
aquiver: trembling
peddler: a person with things to sell
crying his wares: announcing in a loud voice what he has for sale
bespoke: suggested
stare: look intensely and with eyes wide open
off yonder: in the distance

What was it? She did not know; it was too subtle and *elusive* to name.
045> But she felt it, creeping out of the sky, reaching toward her through
the sounds, the scents, the colour that filled the air.

Now her *bosom* rose and fell tumultuously. She was beginning to
recognize this thing that was approaching to possess her, and she was
trying to beat it back with her will—as powerless as her two white
050> slender hands would have been. When she abandoned herself, a little
whispered word escaped her slightly parted lips. She said it over and
over under her breath: "free, free, free!" Her pulses beat fast, and the
coursing blood warmed and relaxed every inch of her body.

She did not stop to ask if it were or were not a monstrous joy that held
055> her. She knew that she would weep again when she saw the kind, tender
hands folded in death; the face that had never looked *save* with love
upon her, fixed and gray and dead. But she saw beyond that bitter
moment a long procession of years to come that would belong to her
absolutely. And she opened and spread her arms out to them in welcome.

060> There would be no one to live for during those coming years; she would
live for herself. There would be no powerful will bending hers in that
blind persistence with which men and women believe they have a right
to impose a private will upon a fellow-creature.

And yet she had loved him—sometimes. Often she had not. What did
065> it matter! What could love, the unsolved mystery, count for in the face
of this possession of self-assertion, which she suddenly recognized
as the strongest impulse of her being!

"Free! Body and soul free!" she kept whispering.

Josephine was kneeling before the closed door with her lips to the keyhole,
070> imploring for admission. "Louise, open the door! I beg; open the door—
you will make yourself ill. What are you doing, Louise? For heaven's sake,
open the door."

"Go away. I am not making myself ill." No; she was drinking in a very
elixir of life through that open window.

075> Her **fancy** was running riot along those days ahead of her. Spring days, and summer days, and all sorts of days that would be her own. She breathed a quick prayer that life might be long. It was only yesterday she had thought with a **shudder** that life might be long.

She arose and opened the door to her sister's **importunities**.
080> There was a feverish triumph in her eyes, and she carried herself like a goddess of Victory. She clasped her sister's waist, and together they descended the stairs. Richards stood waiting for them at the bottom.

Someone was opening the front door with a latchkey. It was Brently Mallard who entered, a little travel-stained, composedly carrying his
085> grip-sack and umbrella. He had been far from the scene of the accident and did not even know there had been one. He stood amazed at Josephine's piercing cry; at Richards' quick motion to screen
090> him from the view of his wife.

But Richards was too late.

When the doctors came, they said she had died of heart disease— of the joy that kills.

Glossary

elusive: difficult to find or catch
bosom: breast; chest
coursing: moving quickly
save: except
elixir: an imaginary remedy for all problems or sicknesses
fancy: imagination
shudder: tremble; shiver
importunities: demands

After Reading

ACTIVITY 1

● Answer the following questions:

a) Why did people "take great care" when they told Mrs. Mallard about her husband's death?

b) The author says that Mrs. Mallard did not "hear" the story like other women might. Instead, she "wept at once with sudden, wild abandonment." What is the author trying to tell us about Mrs. Mallard?

c) Describe Mrs. Mallard's emotional state when she first goes to her room to be alone. (lines 16–32).

d) In lines 33–41, we get a description of her face. Does her age surprise you? What does her face say about her character?

e) Reread lines 42–68. What happens to her in this part of the text?

f) Does this new realization mean that she didn't love her husband? Explain.

g) Her sister implores her to open the door, saying she will make herself ill. How does she think Mrs. Mallard is feeling?

h) After she agrees to leave the room with her sister, someone enters the house. Who is it? Explain the situation.

i) What happens to Mrs. Mallard then?

j) At the beginning of the story, it says she had heart trouble. Do you think this was only a physical problem? Or was it something more? Explain.

ACTIVITY 2

» Find the following lines in the story and explain what the underlined expressions mean:

a) "… to break to her as gently as possible …"

b) "When the storm of grief had spent itself …"

c) "She said it over and over under her breath …"

d) "There would be no powerful will bending hers …"

e) "For heaven's sake, open the door."

ACTIVITY 3

» Chopin uses a lot of imagery to express feelings and thoughts throughout the story. Explain what thoughts and/or feelings the following sentences express:

a) "She could see in the open square before her house the tops of trees that were all aquiver with the new spring life."

b) "The notes of a distant song, which someone was singing, reached her faintly, and countless sparrows were singing in the eaves."

c) "There was a feverish triumph in her eyes, and she carried herself like a goddess of Victory."

Your Thoughts?

a) Identity is an important theme in Chopin's stories. How is it portrayed in "The Story of an Hour?"

b) What do you think Mrs. Mallard's obituary would have been like? Write what you think Josephine, her sister, might have written.

c) Chopin uses imagery to portray feelings of freedom. Imagine you have just been freed from a life of slavery. Using imagery, describe how you feel.

d) Do some research on the rights and conditions of women in the late 1800s. How does the character of Mrs. Mallard compare with women in general during this time period?